Including Children with Speech and Language Delay in the Early Years Foundation Stage

Written by
Antonia Aldous, Aderinola Hotonu
and Ranel Schafer-Dreyer

Consultant
Clare Beswick

Illustrated by
Charlotte Stowell

Reprinted 2010, 2011
Published 2009 by A&C Black Publishers Limited
36 Soho Square, London W1D 3QY
www.acblack.com

ISBN 978-14081-1450-6

Text © Antonia Aldous, Aderinola Hotonu and Ranel Schafer-Dreyer
Illustrations © Charlotte Stowell

**To see our full range of titles
visit www.acblack.com**

Acknowledgements
Special thanks go to Rose Johnson and Christopher Place,
for providing their support for this book and to Bobby's mum.

Contents

Introduction

The Early Years Foundation Stage (EYFS) is an exciting time for all children to create, explore, discover and express themselves as partners in play. Children can explore language as they share in stories, songs and games. The wealth of learning opportunities provided in Early Years settings enables children to experiment with language in play and interactions, and allows them to become more confident in connecting with others and forming positive relationships. It provides them with opportunities to develop the skills necessary to express their needs, desires and interests confidently.

For children with speech and language delay, this may pose challenges. However, with careful and considerate planning, you can ensure that children with speech and language delay also make progress in all areas of the EYFS and feel very much part of the group.

This book aims to provide you with practical tips, activities and advice, as well as giving essential background information on speech and language delay. This in turn should help you to understand the child and their needs better.

Who is this book for?

Although this book is predominantly for Early Years practitioners, it will also be useful for parents and anyone else wanting to support young children. The practical ideas and strategies can be easily adapted or modified to the individual needs of the child, at home or in a group setting, as well as being used for children without speech and language delay.

How this book will help you

This book will inform you by:
- providing essential background information and key facts about speech and language acquisition and delay in the Early Years
- dispelling common myths and answering common questions about speech and language delay
- providing information about the stages of speech and language development
- telling you about the impact of speech and language delay in the Early Years
- alerting you to possible indicators of speech and language delay
- providing you with practical advice on how to maximise a child's communication potential
- signposting you to further resources and organisations.

This book will support you by:
- helping you to create the optimum environment for communication
- showing you how to target the six areas of learning in the EYFS for children with speech and language delay
- suggesting ideas and activities using everyday resources
- giving practical strategies to enable you to develop a child's communication skills
- offering tried and tested tips
- answering questions you may get asked.

This book will motivate you by:
- giving insight into the parent's perspective
- suggesting creative ideas for activities
- equipping you with 'tools' to make it easier for children to understand and respond to you
- describing ways of making a smooth start to the Early Years setting.

This book will make you think by asking:
- What does it feel like to have difficulties in expressing yourself and understanding others?
- What is it like to teach and parent a child with speech and language delay?
- How can I promote effective communication in my setting?

This book will make you ask yourself some questions, such as:
- How can I relate well to this child?
- What do I need to do for this child to enable them to make the most of the EYFS?
- How can I make this child feel self-assured and confident?
- How can I help children to understand, accept, respect and support each other in my setting?
- How can I learn to understand and manage the frustration that comes from communication breakdown?

It will enable a child to:

- have ongoing experiences of being a successful communicator – this will help to enhance a child's social and emotional well-being, and foster a positive disposition and attitude to learning

- play an active role in communicating with others

- understand the world around them

- understand the power of communication to express their needs, interests and desires.

It will enable practitioners and parents to:

- set achievable targets in terms of the EYFS goals

- have realistic expectations about a child's communication abilities

- identify small-step progress and praise accordingly

- adapt their communication level to suit the level of the child

- facilitate the transfer of a child's newly acquired skills to a variety of settings

- adapt their teaching to suit a child's individual learning style, special interests or schemas

- identify a child's strengths and needs, and know when to seek and obtain more specialist advice

- implement positive praise to foster a child's desire to communicate.

This book also aims to reduce child and adult frustration due to communication breakdown, and promote better relationships with others as both the child and adult are empowered during interaction.

The Department for Children, Schools and Families (DCFS) recognises the need for improving services for children with speech, language and communication needs:

'Speech, language and communication are central to each child's potential to be healthy, stay safe, enjoy and achieve, make a positive contribution and ultimately achieve economic well-being.'

www.everychildmatters.gov.uk/aims

The Bercow Report (The Bercow Report: A Review of Services for Children and Young People (0–19) with Speech, Language and Communication Needs), published in July 2008 by the DCSF, reinforces the need to improve services for children with speech, language and communication needs. This is being advocated by the government who intends to invest in a programme called *Every Child a Talker* (ECAT), which will raise Early Years practitioners' awareness of the importance of speech and language. The Bercow Report also articulates the need to raise awareness of speech, language and communication across children's services and explains how to identify and support children with difficulties in these areas.

Our book aims to help and guide you in identifying and supporting children with speech, language and communication needs. It supports key themes identified by the Bercow Report, such as communication being crucial, early identification of delay and intervention being essential, that services support not only the child but also the family, and that joint working with parents and other professionals is essential. We will attempt to be a one-stop shop to parents and practitioners for advice and support strategies.

The activities and ideas in this book:

- are linked to the Early Learning Goals in the EYFS Framework

- are intended to enhance and promote effective communication in a variety of settings

- are easy to implement

- are transferable across settings

- are fun and motivating to all children and adults involved

- take into account the developmental level, learning style and social and emotional well-being of the child

- provide lots of opportunities for step-by-step learning, repetition and positive reinforcement.

Key facts about speech and language delay

What is speech and language delay?

Speech and language delay occurs when a child's communication progress follows a normal pattern of development, but at a slower rate than would be expected for their age. For example, the child might have difficulty understanding others, expressing their wants, interests and desires and/or be difficult to understand. This might cause the child to feel frustrated, lack confidence and they may withdraw socially.

How common is speech and language delay in the UK?

Studies have shown that more than half of children start school with **speech and language delay** but, with the right support, are likely to catch up *(ICAN website, 2009 and The Communication Trust Conference: Developing a Workforce to Support Speech, Language and Communication for all Children, 28th March 2008)*.

Further research estimates that 10% of children have more **long term, persistent communication difficulties** (Lindsay, G. and Dockrell, J. with Mackie, C. and Letchford, B. *Educational Provision for Children with Specific Speech and Language Difficulties in England and Wales*, Cedar and Institute of Education, University of London, 2002). It is estimated that around 6% of children in the UK have 'specific primary speech and language impairments', as opposed to their speech and language difficulties being part of another condition, such as developmental delay, cerebral palsy, fragile X Syndrome and Down's syndrome (Law, J., Boyle, J., Harris, F., Harkness, A. and Nye, C. *Prevalence and Natural History of Primary Speech and Language Delay: Findings from a Systemic Review of the Literature*, IJLCD, vol. 36, 2000).

Specific primary speech and language impairment, alternatively called 'speech and language disorder', refers to a child whose language is not only delayed, but shows some uncharacteristic features (e.g. persistent word-finding difficulties, atypical ordering of words in sentences and significant sound production difficulties and/or unintelligible speech), and additionally does not follow an expected pattern of development. There can also be an uneven profile in relation to the order and rate of speech and language development. More recently, it was reported that around 5 – 7% of children in the UK have specific language impairment (The Communication Trust Conference: *Developing a Workforce to Support Speech, Language and Communication for all Children*, 28th March 2008).
In some areas in the UK, up to 84% of children starting school have **delayed speech and language skills** (www.stokespeaksout.co.uk, 2009).

Studies in areas of social disadvantage have shown that over half of nursery aged children have **language delays** (Locke, A., Ginsborg, J. and Peers, I. *Development and Disadvantage: Implications for Early Years*, IJCLD, vol. 27, no. 1, 2002). This information confirms Foundational Stage profile assessment results. These statistics identify Communication, Language and Literacy as the lowest scoring skills areas for children in the Early Years, well below that considered to be 'a good level of development' (DfES (2005) *Foundation Stage Profile 2005 National Results (Provisional)*, National Statistics Office). These results were supported by the findings of a survey carried out by the Basic Skills Agency. In a UK-wide survey, school staff felt that 50% of children lack the skills that are vital for an effective start to learning (Basic Skills Agency *Summary Report of Survey into Young Children's Skills on Entry to Education,* 2002). These difficulties are thought to be transient and the children should catch up with the right support.

A National Year of Speech, Language and Communication is being planned for 2011/12. Progress in speech, language and communication in children will be reviewed at a national level and further targets and initiatives launched.

What causes speech and language delay?

For a small proportion of children with speech and language delay, there is a clear cause. However, for most children, there appears to be no apparent reason.

Here is a list of possible causes and contributors to children's speech and language delay:

- problems during pregnancy and/or birth

- muscle weakness/low tone, referring to difficulties moving the muscles of the mouth appropriately for speech (lips, tongue and cheeks)

- genetic causes: some communication difficulties may be inherited

- ear infections/glue ear/fluctuating hearing loss

- long-term/permanent hearing loss

- learning difficulties

- syndromes: some children's speech and language difficulties may be part of a recognised syndrome, such as Down's syndrome, fragile X syndrome and cerebral palsy.

It is worth being aware that as many as three times more boys than girls experience speech and language delay.

What is the difference between speech and language?

Speech refers to the way sounds are produced, both on their own and in words or sentences, and how this affects clarity. **Language** can be separated into receptive language/understanding and expressive language/talking.

Receptive language refers to a child's understanding of familiar events (e.g. when they are shown a towel and soap, it implies that it's bathtime), gestures such as pointing, body language and facial expressions (e.g. when mummy is happy she may smile and clap her hands) and other modes of communication, such as signing (e.g. Makaton and British Sign Language) or speaking (e.g. sounds, play sounds, words and sentences).

Expressive language refers to a child's use and expression of language. This can take on different forms, such as making meaningful sounds (e.g. referring to a dog by saying 'woof-woof' and to a car by saying 'beep-beep' or 'brumm-brumm'), producing spoken words and sentences, and having conversations.

It's possible for a child to have either a **speech delay or disorder**, or a **language delay or disorder**, or both together in varying degrees. For example, Sammy, who is four years old, has age-appropriate understanding and talking but substitutes /d/ for /s/ (e.g. he says 'dock' for 'sock'). This means he has only got a speech delay.

Annie, who is five years old, has age-appropriate understanding and clear speech, but finds it difficult to use words in the correct order in a sentence. This might indicate a language disorder and therefore she should be referred to a speech and language therapist.

Delayed versus disordered speech and language

Sometimes, these terms are incorrectly used interchangeably to mean the same thing, that is, to describe a child whose speech and language is developing slower than expected for their age. However, there is a difference!

A child who has **delayed speech and language** tends to make mistakes that would be expected from a younger child. Their speech and language develops slowly but follows a typical pattern of language development.

Speech and language disorder refers to a child's language that is not only severely delayed, but is also atypical and does not follow a normal pattern of development.

It is often difficult to distinguish between speech and language delay and disorder in the Early Years. A delay may resolve itself or present as disordered language later on. A speech and language therapist will be able to assess the child's needs and provide you with support and advice. Many of the activities in this book can be used for disordered speech and language, as well as delayed speech and language.

Dispelling the myths and frequently asked questions

In this chapter, we aim to address common fears and dispell myths about young children with speech and language delay.

'The child is not intelligent'

Speech and language delay is not linked to intelligence!

In its isolated form, where a child has no other developmental delays (physical/learning/social and/or emotional difficulties), with the right input, the child should be able to learn at the same rate as their peers.

When speech and language delay is part of a larger developmental delay, cognition may also be affected, that is, learning and problem-solving skills.

'The child will have these difficulties forever'

With the right input, a child with speech and language delay may in time catch up with their peers. If a child has been diagnosed as having a speech and language disorder, difficulties may persist. (See page 10 for definition.) A speech and language therapist should be able to indicate whether your child has a speech and language delay or disorder.

'What type of school will be best for the child?'

This depends on:

- whether the child has a speech and language delay or disorder

- the severity and persistence of the delay/disorder

- whether the child has additional needs.

The parents will need to seek professional advice when choosing a school for their child. The Special Needs co-ordinator (SENCO) will have guidelines about early support and the educational provision available, and can provide guidance and support to parents in making sure their child's needs are met.

'Can a doctor cure the child?'

The short response to this is: *there is no instant cure!*

All children should make progress with the right professional input and implementation of the activities and strategies outlined in this book, as well as those suggested by a speech and language therapist.

'The child can talk because they can repeat sentences after me'

As adults, we know it is possible to repeat phrases in another language, yet not understand what we are saying. This might be the same for a child who repeats your sentences. They may say the words but lack the understanding and can therefore not use it spontaneously and meaningfully. We therefore recommend that you limit asking a child to repeat what you have said, but rather provide comments on what they are doing.

'Will the child ever talk?'

With a pure speech and language delay, we would expect that, given the appropriate support, the child will develop spoken language. In very young children, it can often be difficult to differentiate between delayed and disordered language. Children with disordered speech and/or language might benefit from alternative communication methods, such as Makaton (a system that uses signed vocabulary to accompany speech), symbols and pictures. A speech and language therapist will be able to advise you further.

'The child will grow out of it and, if not, I can get help when they are older'

In some instances, children may not need extra support to promote their speech and language skills, but may still benefit from the strategies outlined in this book. If there is any concern, it is always better to seek help. Speech and language therapists recommend that difficulties are addressed as early as possible before the gap gets too big. Very young children usually have a greater capacity to learn.

'The child is making up their own language that I can't understand'

Using nonsense words is often referred to as 'jargon', which is typical in normal speech and language development. For children with delayed speech and language skills, this may occur later than expected. Children often use jargon mixed with real words to create conversations during play with peers and adults. Don't be alarmed! Speech and language therapists recommend that you rephrase what you believe they are trying to say.

For example, when the child says 'jargon-jargon-jargon-cat-jargon-jargon', you could interpret the situation and respond with a phrase such as 'cat *sleeping*'(emphasising additional words).

mamo lala ta **cat**

A parent's perspective

Parents may feel shocked, grieved, isolated and helpless when they discover that their child has a communication delay. Knowing the child has a difficulty often raises many questions, such as those discussed in the previous section. However, everyone's experience is unique and no feelings should be dismissed.

In this chapter, we describe one parent's perspective on her experience when she discovered that her child had communication difficulties, and the subsequent journey in helping her child. This story will help you to understand some of the feelings a parent may experience in such a situation, but remember that every parent, as well as every child, is unique.

Bobby's story

(This is a shortened account of an interview with Bobby's mother, focusing on his communication difficulties and his mother's experience of this. All names have been changed.)

Bobby is two and a half years old and attends his local pre-school playgroup for three mornings a week. He also attends Christopher Place (a centre that specialises in pre-school children with communication difficulties) for two afternoons a week where he receives input from a speech and language therapist and occupational therapist. Bobby is on the waiting list for a block of therapy at his local NHS clinic and he also receives weekly individual private therapy.

- **What made you suspect that Bobby had a speech and language delay?**

  Bobby was slow to reach milestones. At 11 months, he said 'mama', but this was all he could say for at least another six months, maybe more. My husband's and my parents were very worried and kept asking us to seek help. We were determined not to be neurotic parents. Initially, we resisted seeking help but eventually, at 18 months old, we took Bobby to a paediatrician who identified several difficulties, including speech and language delay. Bobby's understanding and social development were thought to be age-appropriate.

- **How did this make you feel?**

  It was a kick in the teeth! I had a huge number of questions:
  - Does Bobby have learning difficulties?
  - What does this diagnosis mean?
  - Does he have a condition of some type or another?
  - What has caused this?
  - What does it mean in the short term?
  - What should we be doing?
  - Should we be seeking professional support?
  - What does it mean in terms of his schooling?

- Is he likely to catch up with the other children?
- What are the long-term implications?
- Is he sleeping too much?
- Could the test results just have been due to him not being on form that day?
- Is it due to something I have done?

I think up until that stage, my husband and I had both been in a combination of denial and ignorance that there was a problem. Bobby is our first child and we didn't have a real point of reference of what was 'normal' or expected at his age, so we were relying heavily on the professionals despite the fact that our families were ever more vocal about there being a problem.

- **What did you do when you found out that Bobby had a speech and language delay?**

I set about trying to find a suitable speech and language therapist. At this stage, as Bobby was still only a year and a half old, we didn't really know whether or not he was going to have long-term speech and language problems. I got very busy with research on the internet and looked up everything about helping children with communication difficulties.

Initially we had our therapy sessions very late in the day, just before Bobby's bedtime, which meant that he was very tired and found it difficult to cope with the demands of therapy. We also only had the sessions every couple of weeks, which we felt wasn't really enough.

- **What were your immediate and long-term concerns?**

Suddenly, I wasn't sure if any of my hopes for Bobby were realistic or possible. We were terrified that our child wasn't going to be able to communicate, which felt even more scary. Our concerns keep changing… Although Bobby's speech and language are coming along really well, he still has communication difficulties.

- **Were there any specific issues that you faced, either positive or negative, as you sought advice and managed the situation?**

There are a lot of issues to manage with this kind of situation, but the most difficult one was how to get the best advice from experts and put together a programme that you feel best helps your child. You also have to figure out whose advice to follow and how to sort out and make sense of the overload of information from the internet, professionals, family members etc. It's not always easy to do that in a way that won't offend people or alienate the organisations and people that are trying to help you!

When Bobby was eighteen months old we had another child and the emotional issue of having more than one child and having to focus so much attention on one of them has also been tricky, as you always assume you'll treat both children equally and suddenly one needs you much more. Likewise, giving up a job that I have loved for ten years to concentrate on Bobby for the forseeable future has also been very hard, as I felt that I lost a sense of my own identity when my life became all about my child.

But, on the more positive side, it has also been an incredible experience! The fact that my choices and efforts are likely to make such a difference to my child's life gives what I'm doing with him an amazing importance and makes me very determined! Also, I have a special bond with Bobby as a result of all of this. I'm loving the insight into a world where people have children that aren't 'perfect', but where life still goes on – it makes a lot of the things I used to worry about seem very insignificant and gives me a good sense of perspective. Finally, finding out about the different approaches is an enormous learning curve and very fascinating. If it wasn't all completely emotionally terrifying, I think I'd be loving this experience!

- **Were there any significant responses from family members or friends? Have they adapted their interaction style with Bobby?**

Both my husband and my family are incredible and I am exceptionally lucky in this respect. We also have amazing friends who seem to understand the issue (even though they don't really know the ins and outs in the same way as our families). They love spending time with Bobby – because frankly, in my slightly biased opinion, he is a lot of fun, incredibly sociable and can, on the whole, express himself better with his gestures and mannerisms than many kids of his age can do with their speech. On the whole, I don't really see them change their attitude to Bobby because of his difficulties, but then he is still very young, so I worry that they may do so as he gets older.

- **Has anyone underestimated what Bobby is capable of or interacted with him as if he were a much younger child?**

I think this is the big danger and one of my greatest worries with having a child with communication delays. Mostly, I think people can see fairly quickly that he 'gets it'. I'm with him most of the time, so certainly I'd never let anyone patronise him or pitch things at the wrong level when I'm around. I will also try to make sure that when I do leave him, for example, at mainstream nursery, the staff are well informed to make sure this doesn't happen.

- **What advice would you give to other parents whose children may have speech and language delay or difficulties?**

    Lots of thoughts…
    - I would suggest that you try to find out exactly what it is that you're dealing with, to the extent that you are able to do so – and then get on top of it.
    - Find the best possible therapists that you can. Make sure that they understand and specialise in your child's difficulties. Make sure that you monitor progress and that things are moving forward the whole time. If they aren't, then look at what your options are.
    - Incorporate all the therapy activities into your way of life. For example, Bobby's lip and tongue muscles are weak which affects his speech clarity so we have been advised to practise blowing whistles and sucking through straws to develop his lip and tongue muscles. We have a bowl of whistles on the table every time Bobby waits for his meals.

We encourage him to blow bubbles through straws with all his drinks. He also 'drinks' his yoghurt through straws, eats chewy food and I always give him options to choose from (so not just 'yes' and 'no' answers). I also do therapy sessions with him on the days that he doesn't have a therapy session. I have taken photos of lots of people he knows pulling different faces and we play a game where he has to copy their faces.

- Do whatever it is that helps you to achieve what you're trying to do, no matter how silly it makes you feel or how much it doesn't fit in with what people consider to be good manners. I try to make the therapy as fun as possible and it helps that I am not worried about humiliating myself. I didn't have any issues with him wiggling on my tummy pretending to be a worm to practise the 'w' sound if it works (and it did!). It may be best not to do it in public, but you might as well make it fun if you're both stuck doing it.

- His older cousin comes round (who has no issue with his speech) to play 'talking games' and the two of them play all these slightly bizarre games that I've created so that Bobby can practise saying the stuff I want him to work on. Thankfully, his older cousin hasn't yet cottoned on to the fact that it's a little strange. Bobby adores him and wants to copy everything he does!

- I have acquired lots of toys that I think are really helpful for speech development, for example, a keyring that records and plays back speech so he can hear what he has just said, a microphone to encourage him to talk and games that feature characters he likes from television etc. (Your local toy library will have toys that you can borrow. For further information, you can contact your local library.)

- I think it's important to research the options for Early Years provision and beyond. For us, combining an incredible place for therapy such as Christopher Place, with a mainstream nursery was the best option.

- We use fish oils in cooking every day, but please check with your health worker or family doctor.

- I've spent a load of time on the internet speaking to mothers going through the same issues as me. I find it an incredible way to get information, as long as you don't rely on everything that's said, but to listen to advice and then verify it.

- I have read loads of useful books. Books you may find useful include *It Takes Two to Talk – A Parent's Guide to Helping Children Communicate* by Ayala Manolson (Hanen Publication, ISBN 0-921145-02-0) and *You Make the Difference: In Helping Your Child Learn* by Ayala Manolson with Barb Ward and Nancy Dodington (Hanen Publication, ISBN 0-921145-06-3).

Parent partnership

Bobby's mother's account highlights the need for parents and Early Years practitioners to work in partnership, sharing aims and targets that can be integrated into the different settings that the child attends. As well as the need for professionals to share their knowledge and expertise, it is also vital that parents voice their concerns and make choices based on the information they are given.

Speech and language therapists must fulfil their role in providing specialist knowledge, and equipping parents and practitioners with strategies and activities. Parents know their child best and are therefore an essential source of information and should be considered as partners in this process.

Early Years practitioners and other professionals involved can support children with speech and language delay by using strategies outlined in the 'Rapper's Way' (see page 33).

Early Years practitioners and other professionals involved can support parents by:

- making time to regularly listen and discuss the child's progress, and talk about concerns
- collaborating respectfully with other professionals to support all aspects of the child's learning
- contributing in multi-agency meetings
- keeping accurate and up-to-date records on all aspects of the child's development and progress.

Indicators of speech and language delay

How do I know if a child's speech and language is delayed?

Consider the tables 'Stages of speech and language development' on pages 70 – 75, but please note that these must be interpreted with caution. Every child develops at different rates. Any child may be momentarily outside the norm in one or more areas of their development, this may be because they are going through acceleration or delay in that area, which is as would be expected. Careful observation and record keeping over a period of time are important to gain a full picture of the child's communication profile.

It may be that the child is more delayed in one of the areas of speech and language development. For example, the child may have appropriate attention and listening skills, mildly delayed play skills and understanding, and more severely delayed expressive language, with or without a speech sound difficulty. This can be ascertained through careful observation and record keeping, as well as talking to and liaising with parents and professionals who work with the child, looking back at their progress and observing their communication in a variety of settings. It's helpful to visit the child at home to get a sense of the family circumstances and home environment. Similarly, if the child attends two Early Years settings, it can be useful to visit and discuss their development and progress in both placements.

All areas of learning and development interplay and may affect one another. For example, the development and use of language depends on attaining certain thinking, play, social and motor skills. Speech requires the physical growth and control of oral muscles.

If you are concerned that a child has a delay in any area of speech and langauge development and/or has difficulties in at least two areas from the checklist on the following page, then we advise that you seek professional help from your local speech and language therapist, SENCO or Early Years support worker.

Is the child:

- showing signs of frustration?

- being socially excluded by peers?

- avoiding engaging with other adults and/or children?

- demonstrating delayed play skills when compared to peers?

- using a lot of gesture, pointing and or vocalisations to express needs and interests when compared to peers?

- scoring outside the age norms when looking at speech and language developmental charts?

- finding it difficult to learn and remember new vocabulary?

- using the incorrect word order?

- using sentences that are shorter and less complex than peers?

- having difficulty understanding age-appropriate questions?

- passive or withdrawn, or alternatively disruptive?

- anxious in a noisy and/or group setting?

- finding it difficult to choose an activity?

- finding it difficult to remain focused on an activity of their choice?

- struggling to express needs and interests?

Remember every child has a unique personality and learning style, so try to avoid constantly comparing children. Each child's rate of progress varies and may be affected by a number of inter-related factors. It's possible to enhance a child's progress and develop their confidence and interest by considering the following suggestions. Try to be flexible and creative in the approaches you use to teach new skills.

It may be helpful to consider...

- the child's **learning style**. For example, ask yourself: Is s/he predominantly a visual learner? Would s/he benefit from visual timetables, pictures and symbols? Does s/he need daily repetition of new ideas and concepts? Is his/her learning helped by gestures, Makaton signing and/or pointing?

- **prompts** that aid the child's learning. For example, auditory cues, such as calling the child's name before an instruction/comment is given and physical prompts, such as touching the child to gain attention, or maybe gently touching the child's face to encourage eye contact.

- the child's **interests**. For example, ask yourself: is the child interested in animals, sport or food? Learning can be focused on any particular topics of interests to the child.

- the child's **family and friends**. People who are close to the child could be included in supporting the child, reinforcing new concepts and ideas, and encouraging generalisation of skills. Family and friends can be effective motivators and useful for encouraging the child.

- the child's **culture**. Children from different cultures may have experiences and traditions that need to be considered and included when planning activities.

- **what motivates** the child, for example, stickers, stamps, badges, clapping, verbal praise etc. Praising and rewarding the child's attempts meaningfully will encourage persistence and help to develop self-confidence.

Learning should be a positive experience, and fun and rewarding for each child and all those involved in supporting them. Allow yourself and the child to enjoy their successes and achievements together.

Babies and speech and language delay

Speech and Language delay in babies and toddlers may be difficult to diagnose. Additionally, communication difficulties may not yet be apparent at the early stages of a child's development. In the first year of life there is considerable variability in the rate of communication development. You should therefore be cautious about labelling babies as having speech and language delay. The first year of a child's life should be a time to focus on establishing a bond between the baby and parents/carers.

However, we strongly advise that you tell parents to seek advice from the baby's health visitor, G.P., local speech and language therapist or early years support worker if they display obvious signs of communication difficulties. Such difficulties could include:

- The absence of babbling
- Lack of response to sound
- Lack of interest in the environment
- Difficulties feeding (eating and drinking)
- Lack of pointing or attempting to reach out to objects or familiar people
- Not recognising familiar faces, voices and objects
- The absence of facial expression
- Lack of response to human contact
- Significant passivity

It is likely that these difficulties form part of another condition (e.g. a medical condition, a recurrent illness, a learning difficulty or a hearing impairment) and are not the result of a pure speech and language delay. In addition, the child may also display difficulties in other areas of development such as movement.

Even though babies do not talk or appear to understand much, this is the stage in which foundation skills for communication begin to develop. These skills include:

- Awareness of sounds
- Babbling
- Object permanence
- Joint attention
- Eye contact
- Turn-taking
- Play
- Situational understanding

The following section looks at each of these early communication skills in more detail and provides you with ideas and activities to facilitate their development in babies.

Awareness of sounds

From birth, a hearing baby will be aware of the sounds and noises in their environment, such as doors slamming, dogs barking etc. As the baby matures and their hearing develops the ability to detect quieter sounds, differentiate and identify sounds improves. Their response to sounds may be variable; they may laugh or alternatively stop crying when they hear their mother's voice. For children with hearing difficulties, their responses to sound may be less predictable. If you are concerned about your babies' hearing, consult a Health Visitor or G.P.

Activities to do with babies:

To develop a baby's auditory awareness and attention:

- When you hear a sound in the environment such as a police car, a dog barking, the phone ringing or water running, point to your ear, say "Listen", label the sound and point to it.
- In face-to-face contact with the baby make a variety of simple sounds (e.g. 'babababa' or 'tatatata'). Alternate between making exaggerated lip patterns with and without sound.
- When the baby has sufficient head control to rotate their head and sit unsupported (roughly around 6-9 months), you can make a noise (e.g. shake a bell) behind them to one side. Encourage them to turn to the sound and immediately reward their attempt.

To develop exposure to sound:

- Sing songs to your baby during everyday routines, e.g. make up a washing song for bath time.
- Expose the baby to noisy and pop-up toys and instruments and play with them.

Babbling

The use of voice in the form or crying is often the first sound a baby makes. Babies soon start using their voice for other reflex actions such as yawning, coughing and sneezing.

Next, at around two months, they begin to laugh, coo and make sounds of pleasure. During this time they begin to use simple sustained vowel sounds such as 'ahhhh', followed later by consonant sounds such as 'p' and 'b'. These sounds are learnt through self exploration and not through imitation. Vocal play increases but has no communicative intent. Babies also start to play with and explore sounds in different combinations.

From six months babies start to reduplicate sounds such as 'badadado', 'babu', 'mama'. This is referred to as 'babbling'. At this stage they are still unable to imitate sounds but will respond vocally to spoken interactions. Initially the sounds have no attached meaning. As babies' vocalizations develop their babbling begins to sound more like words. These are referred to as 'proto-words'. Eventually proto-words have attached meaning, e.g. when the baby points to a baby or a doll and vocalises 'baba'. This is different from the babble stage where the baby is only exploring sounds. Proto-words develop into real words over time.

Babble is important in developing:

- Sound production
- The auditory feedback loop (i.e. the ability to self monitor vocal productions)
- Mouth movements for speech
- Understanding of the effect that their voice has on their environment and those in it
- Social interactions
- Expression of emotions

Activities to do with babies:

- Repeat back the sounds the baby makes with animated facial expressions and enthusiasm.
- Get the baby to look at you while you make up different vocalizations using changes in pitch, volume and rhythm.

Object permanence

This refers to the ability to understand that an object still exists even when it cannot be seen, felt, smelt or heard any longer. This skill is important for cognitive and language development (i.e. thinking, learning and understanding).

This skill develops in stages but is generally fully established by nine months.

Activities to do with babies:

- Play 'Peek-a-Boo'.
- Let the baby see you hide a motivational toy under a blanket. Then create intrigue and anticipation as to where the toy has gone. Enthusiastically reveal the toy again and play with it.

Joint attention

For babies, joint attention refers to the ability to share their attention with another person or focus jointly on an object or play activity. This skill is usually fully established by nine to twelve months. From birth, engage in daily face-to-face contact with the baby whereby your baby is sitting on your lap facing you.

Activities to do with babies:

- Use highly motivating toys to gain attention such as noisy toys, toys that light up or are brightly coloured.
- Make funny faces at the baby. Pause after each expression while encouraging the baby to copy you.
- Use your fingers to attract the baby's attention, wiggling them in front of the babies' face and stroking his/her cheeks. Praise with smiles and gestures.
- Use songs and interesting voices such as "Round and Round the Garden" and "This Little Piggy went to the Market" to engage the baby with.

Eye contact

Eye contact is another important component of social interaction which starts to develop very early on in the baby's life. This can also be facilitated during direct face-to-face contact with your baby.

Activities to do with babies:

- Gradually move closer to the baby's face and engage in different physical activities such as gently blowing on the side of their face, touching/tickling/stroking their cheek, whispering their name and smiling at them.

Turn-taking

This develops in the first year of life and is a prerequisite for effective conversations and social interactions. It refers to the ability to take turns in activities and social exchanges. For babies the reciprocal nature of turn-taking is often best achieved through face-to-face contact with the adult.

Activities outlined in both joint attention and eye contact can also be used to develop turn-taking skills.

More activities to do with babies:

- Roll a ball back and forth.
- Activate a toy by tapping/pushing/touching/feeling.
- Pop bubbles.
- Name whose turn it is, e.g. "Mummy's turn" and "Ben's turn" and point to the named person.

Play

For more information on the early stages of play development, refer to the play section on page 50. By developing play, babies learn more about their environment and world, develop language and learn how to interact socially.

Situational understanding

Situational understanding begins at birth. Before babies are able to understand real words and sentences they need to develop an understanding of their environment. This is known as situational understanding. Examples of situational understanding include a baby knowing that he will be fed when the parent/carer approaches with a spoon or knowing that it is bath time when they see a towel.

The baby does not necessarily understand the words but rather what the objects represent. Gradually babies will begin to understand frequently used words that represent objects and actions.

Tips for developing babies' language

- Talk to babies to help develop their language and shape their speech sounds.
- Ensure your language is simple, repetitive and interesting with appropriate pauses.
- Provide babies with routines, which they enjoy anyway. This will help develop their situational understanding.
- When babies babble, copy them and wait in anticipation for them to respond. In this way a simple 'conversation' is occurring.
- Shape babies' speech sounds to encourage them to make first words. For example, if the baby says "mamamama" when looking at the mother, the mother should repeat back "yes, it's mummy." In this way the baby will hear the adult model of the real word.

The first year of a baby's life is a very exciting time when development in all areas happens rapidly. It's a time when they are absorbing lots of information from their surroundings. It's therefore important to provide babies with appropriate activities to stimulate them and facilitate their learning.

Most importantly, remember to enjoy this precious time with them!

Speech and language delay and the six areas of the EYFS

Young children with speech and language delay may have more difficulty in some areas of learning than others. However, it is likely that their difficulties will impact upon all areas of learning and development in the EYFS. Each of the six areas pose their own set of challenges to children with speech and language delay.

Personal, Social and Emotional Development

Personal, Social and Emotional Development (PSED) focuses on relationships and understanding the needs of others. PSED helps children to develop a positive sense of themselves and others, and encourages them to express their feelings and emotions in a positive way.

Children with speech and language delay will inevitably be faced with a unique set of challenges. They are often unable to express themselves to, or be understood by, others, and therefore sometimes have difficulties in forming relationships and bonds. They experience frequent breakdowns in their communications. This acts as a barrier to positive social interactions, undermines confidence and reduces ability and sometimes willingness to learn.

How can Early Years practitioners support children in this area of the EYFS?

- Establish strong, appropriate relationships with and between children. This can be achieved by modelling sharing, turn-taking and greetings in routine group activities, such as snack time and home time. During group games, model good turn-taking – rolling balls, putting clothes on a doll, taking objects out of a box etc.

- Value and encourage what children can do and their own originality. Use specific praise, prompts and encouragement to respond to children's attempts to communicate and carry out activities. Specific praise refers to commenting accurately and honestly on what the child has done well, for example, 'good colouring inside the lines!' and 'thank you very much for carrying the cups!'.

- Encourage the children to value different religions and cultures. Focus activities on stories around different festivals, such as Christmas, Diwali and Ramadan.

- Establish relationships with parents and involved professionals. Encourage parents to write in home school books. If appropriate, you could invite them to attend a session and/or come in to discuss their child's progress. Similarly, it's important to create good relationships with other professionals working with the child. This may be done through regular telephone correspondence, sharing reports and attending joint meetings.

Communication, Language and Literacy

The ability to communicate effectively is the key to successful learning and to life. Children with speech and language delay will be challenged at all levels. They may have difficulties with attention and listening, understanding and use of language and/or speech sounds. They may also struggle with literacy skills. They will need careful observation and assessment to accurately identify the particular area of delay (speech, understanding, use of language, attention and listening, or social interaction). This should be followed by a comprehensive individual plan focused on addressing the child's needs. Some children may require support with turn-taking, sharing and developing play – both adult-directed play and child-led play.

For other children, support may be needed for developing their expressive and receptive vocabulary, helping them to express their ideas and interests, and build social relationships. These children, more than other children, will require a rich offer of creative, dynamic activities suited to their needs, such as music, dance, painting, early writing, modelling, storytelling and singing.

How can Early Years practitioners support children in this area of the EYFS?

- Create opportunities for children to develop language and communication through play, music, storytelling, songs, dance, painting, ICT and so on.

- Encourage role play of familiar stories using costumes and props. Encourage the children to take on different roles and characters. You may need to model language.

- Sing action songs together – 'Incy Wincy Spider', 'Row, Row, the Boat', 'The Wheels on the Bus' and so on. Songs and music can also be a helpful tool for teaching concepts and new vocabulary, such as colour songs, number songs and so on.

- Encourage the children to look at books to build up an awareness of text and the idea that written words convey meaning, i.e. early literacy skills. When they are ready, children can be encouraged to create their own stories around themes and tell them to the class during circle time. Children can also be encouraged to play verbal or written consequence-type games, where each child adds a new line to the story.

- Use dance and movement, which can be a motivating tool, for teaching concepts such as positional words (in, on, under, through, up, down and so on), and adjectives and adverbs, such as small, quietly, loudly, softly and so on.

- Set up painting activities, which is an excellent way of introducing the concept of colour, shape, texture and new vocabulary.

- Use ICT and video to develop language, literacy and communication. Video can also be a concrete way of monitoring children's development and progress.

Children with speech and language delay often need more time to process information and to formulate their answers. It is therefore important to allow them extra time to respond to instructions and comments.

Problem Solving, Reasoning and Numeracy

All children need a broad range of activities to help them to explore, enjoy and learn.

Being able to sort, match, order, sequence, predict and compare are all foundation skills for good problem solving, reasoning and numeracy. Children can discover things about their environment, for example, shapes, distances and numbers. These early mathematical concepts and the accompanying vocabulary provide children with language that can be used to describe how things relate in their environment.

Children with speech and language delay often have difficulties in this area – understanding and processing the new vocabulary, remembering the new concepts and words, predicting outcomes, problem solving and generalising what they have learnt from other settings.

How can Early Years practitioners support children in this area of the EYFS?

- Give children sufficient time to process the new vocabulary and concepts. Pause between sentences and allow the child extra time for responding to instructions, comments and questions.

- Revisit and repeat the new vocabulary and concepts frequently, and in a variety of different activities. For example, if you are teaching new concepts such as 'bigger' and 'smaller,' at snack time you can compare the size of fruits; when lining up, you can compare the size of the children; when building Lego towers, you can compare the size of the towers; when looking at your fingers, you can compare the size of your fingers etc. Children with speech and language delay often find it difficult to remember and generalise new concepts and vocabulary. Variety and frequent repetition are keys for successful learning in this area of the EYFS.

- Encourage the children to explore real-life situations and come up with solutions for everyday events, such as how many cups you need for snack time, how many pieces of cake you need if everyone wants a piece, and how many pages of a book are left to read. Teach the concepts of 'half,' 'whole,' 'bigger' and 'smaller' when cutting up apples and so on.

Make sure everyone gets half

- Use indoor and outdoor environments where possible as this will help the children to generalise their new skills as well as providing further interest and learning opportunities.

Knowledge and Understanding of the World

Children need to make sense of the world. They need to develop knowledge, skills and understanding about the world in which they live. Through play-based activities centred on themselves and their immediate world, they explore what they see, hear and feel, and try to make sense of this.

Children with speech and language delay often have delayed play skills, which may hinder their ability to express their wants, likes and dislikes in relation to their place in the world. By developing their play, these children learn more about their environment and world; they develop language and learn how to interact socially.

How can Early Years practitioners support children in this area of the EYFS?

- Model new and varied aspects of play. Provide demonstrations of how to use different objects and materials in a meaningful way, for example, encourage the child to look at you while you pretend to brush your own hair, then the hair of a doll, before offering the brush to the child, encouraging them to copy your actions. Involve children in everyday activities, such as washing/feeding and dressing a baby or doll, wiping the table and washing the dishes. Use simple language to accompany your actions, for example, 'Baby drinking/eating', 'Washing baby' and so on.

- Encourage the children to explore different materials and textures, such as water, sand, play dough, shaving foam, pastry etc. Place objects in the water for children to play with, encourage them to draw pictures, letters or numbers in shaving foam, roll out pastry and press out shapes with cutters etc. Many children with speech and language delay will be reluctant to explore new media, sticking to what they understand and know best. Peers, key persons and parents can be useful in modelling and encouraging children to explore new materials.

- Explore toys and objects from different cultures and religions. Dress up in different costumes from around the world, look at books on religions and cultures, and have themed days where you try food from different cultures.

  Children with speech and language delay will benefit from experiential learning by being actively involved in activities rather than sitting and listening to facts about the world. These types of activities provide opportunities for the Early Years practitioner to introduce and reinforce new vocabulary and ideas.

- Talk about feelings, likes and dislikes. For children with speech and language delay, it is helpful to use visual aids to facilitate their understanding and expression of emotions and feelings. For example, use symbols and gestures, draw pictures and act out simple emotions, such as happy, sad, scared and surprised. Make collages or simple scrapbooks using photos and pictures torn from magazines while encouraging the child to express feelings and emotions.

  Set up opportunities where the child can express preferences and make choices by using their established skills, such as pointing, gesturing, signing and using single words or sentences. For example, make sandwiches at lunch time and let the children choose fillings and express likes and dislikes in food. This will develop the child's confidence to use language and express emotions independently and spontaneously. Take every opportunity to offer real choices.

- Encourage the children to explore a range of different technologies and programmable toys, for example, a Bee Bot and Roamer (both programmable floor robots), remote control cars and an adapted keyboard with picture symbols to help with letter recognition. Early Years practitioners should select and adapt equipment to enable a child with speech and language delay to fully utilise the technology in an appropriate way. For example, choose appealing equipment that is simple to use, such as interactive whiteboards on which the child can see an immediate response to their actions. Using a modified PC screen and mouse can aid independent use of ICT equipment. Children with speech and language delay often gravitate towards these types of activities since they require less social interaction and verbal communication. It is essential that their time is monitored and, where possible, the activities are made as interactive as possible. Using Walkie Talkies, microphones and Talking Tins can be fun ways of encouraging the child with speech and language delay to communicate with peers and adults. Early Years practitioners should make sure children use a combination of ICT activities to encourage both independent exploration and social communication.

Physical Development

Children need to be active and interactive, and able to develop the skills of co-ordination, control, manipulation and movement. This area of learning and development in the EYFS refers to a child's ability to move in a co-ordinated way with control and strength. It also includes the child's ability to understand the importance of physical activity and healthy choices in relation to food.

Children with a pure speech and language delay don't usually have difficulties with gross motor movement, co-ordination, body control or strength, but may have difficulties with the movement of their tongue, lips, jaw and/or mouth. Difficulties with blowing whistles/bubbles, sucking through straws and unclear speech may be indicative of this. Weakness in the mouth area may also be part of a more global body muscle weakness, in which case a referral to an occupational therapist as well as to a speech and language therapist is recommended.

Some children with speech and language delay may have additional physical difficulties that are not part of their communication delay. The child's physiotherapist or occupational therapist can provide advice.

How can Early Years practitioners support children in this area of the EYFS?

Physical activities can provide a fun and interactive way of teaching new vocabulary, ideas and concepts. For example, when the children are jumping on trampolines, comment on their action with language at the appropriate level, for example, 'jump, jump, jump' or 'Bobby's jumping up and down'. Using commentary is a valuable tool for teaching and consolidating new language, especially for children with speech and language delay.

Early Years practitioners should ensure that their commentary is:

- meaningful i.e. it should accompany the action of the child.

- immediate so that the children can link the words to their actions.

- at the child's language level i.e. if the child is using single words in their own speech, the Early Years practitioners should comment on actions by using one to two words repetitively. For example, when going up steps, say 'Walk up', 'Climbing up' or 'going upstairs'.

Accompanying commentary with natural gestures, signs, exaggerated intonation patterns (i.e. using an interesting voice) and symbolic noises (e.g. saying 'weeeee' when the child goes down a slide) can facilitate their language learning further.

Creative Development

Children should be given opportunities to extend their creativity, and explore and share their thoughts in a variety of ways – through movement, art and crafts, role play and design and technology.

Children with speech and language delay often have difficulties in the area of creative development. They may find it difficult to imagine and role play, to remember stories and songs, and to express and communicate their ideas effectively. Once again, creative activities are wonderful opportunities to introduce and consolidate new language and ideas for children with speech and language delay.

How can Early Years practitioners support children in this area of the EYFS?

- Encourage children to listen to and create music. Provide them with instruments to play, either in a child-initiated activity or in an adult-directed group activity. Encourage them to take turns banging drums, to listen and copy simple rhythms, to detect whether sounds are loud or quiet and to move to fast and slow beats. Playing musical bumps and musical statues can be fun ways to develop attention and listening skills. 'Pass the Parcel' to music is another fun way of developing listening and turn-taking. Encourage language when labelling the prize in each wrapper.

- Make up songs or change the words in well-known rhymes, such as 'Humpty Dumpty sat on a ball' and 'Twinkle, twinkle, little car'. Encourage the children to come up with their own suggestion, either independently or in groups. Remember to praise, prompt and reward attempts.

- Encourage the children to explore different rhythms, pitches and types of music – fast, slow, loud, quiet, classical, jazz etc. – and dance accordingly.

- Encourage the children to act out stories and take on different roles and characters – to use different voices and mannerisms. Story sacks, puppets and props can also be used to act out stories and scenarios. The children will need to be very familiar with the stories and therefore it's essential that they have heard them many times before. When role playing, the Early Years practitioner may need to supply language models to the children. Children with speech and language delay may need to be prompted when acting out stories. They may need to be reminded to take their turn, to use the correct emotions and to use sound effects appropriately etc. These prompts could take the form of gestures, facial expressions, sign, touching and verbal cues.

- Use resources and artefacts from different cultures and religions, such as banjos and other musical instruments from around the world, quill pens and writing tools from the past etc. Discuss what they could be used for and if possible, practise using them. Encourage the children to bring in their own objects to show and discuss in 'show and tell' type activities. These activities are fun, enjoyable and useful language learning opportunities for all children. However, for children with speech and language delay, it's essential that language is adapted to their level, sentences are kept short, and new vocabulary is repeated and accompanied with an experience, action or object. For example, when playing with a quill pen, introduce words such as 'feather', 'soft' and 'light' while encouraging the children to explore these properties with the pen.

- When engaged in active play, both inside and outside, allow the children to explore two-dimensional and three-dimensional objects – to crawl through tunnels, go down slides, stack large bricks, play on swings, walk along low beams etc. Provide language for encouragement and simple commentary for actions, such as 'down slide' when going down a slide, 'push swing' while on the swing and 'head up, arms out' when walking on low beams.

Early Years settings pose unique challenges and opportunities to children with speech and language delay, as they are often busy and at times noisy with many children all with individual needs. Early Years practitioners need to identify and provide ongoing support. Through a flexible approach and with the suggestions outlined in this section, it should be possible to support and include children with speech and language delay in all six areas of learning and development in the EYFS. Many of our suggested activities can be carried out in a group with the everyday, familiar resources and equipment often already found in the Early Years setting.

Practitioners making a difference – what can I do to help?

As Early Years practitioners, we have many roles: teaching, organising, listening, supporting, comforting, encouraging, reassuring, telling stories, playing, supervising, observing, helping, caring and so on. Sometimes we forget that each of these roles creates situations that can be wonderful learning opportunities. How we make use of the environment and our language impacts greatly upon the children's speech and language development. By making simple changes when playing and talking to children, we can make significant improvements to their development of understanding and their use of language.

Key strategies to engage children with speech and language delay in the EYFS can be summarised by 'The Rapper's Way' *(Rose Johnson – Christopher Place Speech, Language and Hearing Centre):*

'The RAPPER'S Way'

- **R**educe questions
- **A**dd commentary
- **P**raise and rephrase
- **P**ause and allow
- **E**xpand
- **R**epeat
- **S**implify

Reduce questions

As Early Years practitioners, it is often our natural instinct to ask questions about what our children are doing, seeing and experiencing. We often ask questions such as 'What is this?', 'What colour/shape/size is that?' and 'What are you doing?'.

For children to respond appropriately, they need to understand the concepts used, remember and process the sentence, and formulate a response. For children with speech and language delay, this is a tall order and may provoke anxiety.

They will actually learn more from your comments than from answering questions at this stage. By commenting on what they are interested in, you are providing them with a motivating language experience that they are more likely to learn from. Therefore, it is better to **reduce the number of questions** you ask children with speech and language delay during this important language learning period of a child's life, for example:

Scenario 1: A child plays with a doll that has just fallen off the table.

Adult response: Instead of 'What's dolly doing?', say 'Dolly fall down'.

Scenario 2: A child is kicking a ball.

Adult response: Instead of 'What are you doing?', say 'Kick ball'.

Scenario 3: A child puts a ball in a bag.

Adult response: Instead of 'Where are you putting the ball?', say 'Ball in'.

Scenario 4: A child is playing with a yellow car while you want to target colour concepts.

Adult response: Instead of 'What colour is the car?', say 'Brummm brummm, yellow car.'

Add commentary

Everyday routines and activities at home and in the Early Years setting provide excellent language learning opportunities due to their repetitiveness and predictability. Activities, such as going upstairs, washing hands, meals, snack time and circle time, as well as outside play, are all excellent opportunities to comment on what children are doing. Commenting on children's immediate environment and interests gives them the language they need to enable them to express their interests, desires and needs for example:

Scenario 1: A child, who is at a pre-verbal stage, is playing with a duck toy.

Adult response: 'Quack quack'.

Scenario 2: A child, who is at a pre-verbal/single word level, is walking up the stairs or pointing upwards. Children who are pre-verbal mainly use sounds to communicate meaning, for example, using 'woof-woof' to refer to a dog and 'choo-choo' to refer to a train.

Adult response: 'Up, Up, Up'.

Scenario 3: A child, who uses single words or two-word sentences, is getting dressed.

Adult response: 'Socks/shoes/shirt on'.

Scenario 4: A child, who can use two- or three-word sentences, is eating a banana.

Adult response: 'Johnny eating banana'.

Praise and rephrase

Children with speech and language delay tend to find it difficult to express themselves accurately. They may lack the words, find it difficult to formulate their ideas and/or have unclear speech. Communication may be a struggle for them.

As an Early Years practitioner/key person, you need to actively encourage and praise children's communication attempts. By praising and rephrasing children's utterances, you are acknowledging that you've understood them but are also providing them with the correct model, for example:

Scenario 1: A child says 'bish' instead of 'fish'.

Adult response: Praise the attempt and rephrase it, for example, 'Yes, it's a *fish*' (emphasising the new sound).

Scenario 2: A child says 'eeeeerrrrrr bus'.
Adult response: Respond with 'Yes, you're right, it's a *red* bus', emphasising the new word.

Your praise could be verbal, for example, 'good talking', 'nice idea' and 'yes', or gestural, such as clapping, thumbs up, smiling or cuddling. Once children feel they are successful communicators, they are more likely to attempt new words and phrases.

Value children with speech and language delay as communicators, regardless of the mistakes they make.

Praise, prompts and rewards

When you work with children with speech and language delay, it is useful to think of praise, prompts and rewards as essential tools.

You can actively **plan, monitor and record** your use of praise, rewards and prompts by:

- **trialling** different rewards, such as stickers, stamps, badges, verbal praise and clapping, and prompts including calling the child's names before instructing them, touching them to gain their attention, gently touching their faces to encourage eye contact or pointing to encourage joint attention. Try this with a child in a range of activities and over a period of time to find out what motivates them best. Remember that what motivates one child might not be rewarding for another.

- **monitoring** how praise, rewards and prompts are used with specific children. This can be done by keeping a record of what kind of praise, rewards and prompts were used over a period of time.

- **adapting** your use of rewards and prompts where necessary to best motivate and engage the child.

Pause and allow

As Early Years practitioners, we often need to take control of the children's environment, protecting them from danger and helping them with meal times, dressing and other personal care needs. It can sometimes be all too easy to slip into the habit of directing their play, and not allowing them to pursue their own ideas and interests. By encouraging child-initiated activities rather than adult-directed activities, you are allowing children to express their feelings, needs and interests. This also allows you to get to know the children and discover what motivates them.

Be more responsive to children's needs and engage in child-led activities by:

- **pausing and keeping quiet**. This will take the pressure off the children and allow them to take control and explore their own interests. Aim for companionable quiet time together.

- **looking, listening and noting** what the children are saying and doing.

- **responding**, at their level, to what they are doing and saying.

Expand

This strategy refers to you expanding children's spoken language and the length of their sentences. This could refer to spoken language or signing.

As an Early Years practitioner you need to be very clear about a child's expressive language levels before you attempt to expand on their language.

How can you determine a child's expressive language level?

- Look, listen and note what the child's spontaneous speech and language is like during play and interacting with others. Write down exactly what they say and how they express their needs, wants and interests. For example, ask yourself if they are indicating preferences by eye-pointing or finger-pointing; using natural gesture such as waving, and leading adults to desired objects of interest.

Also ask yourself:

- Are they being silent when expressing themselves or using vocalisations to accompany gestures and signs?

- Are they using play sounds such as 'choo-choo', 'brumm-brumm' and 'yum-yum'?

- Are they using single words to label common objects and actions, for example, 'shoe', 'jumping' and 'sleeping'?

- Are they joining two words together, for example, 'more juice', 'mummy sleeping' and 'dolly jumping'?

- Are they using longer phrases to communicate?

It is also important to note:

- Whether their expressions are spontaneous or imitated.

- Whether their expressions are meaningful, for example, are they using nonsense words or real words?

- Whether they are generalising expressions from one setting and/or activity to another, or only using them in one particular setting and/or activity.

- The number of words they use.

- The types of words and sentences (e.g. action words, object names and descriptive words etc.).

- How often, where, when and with whom different words are used?

- The clarity of words and sentences.

- Whether the words are used in the correct order in sentences, for example, is the child saying, 'Daddy mummy whispering' instead of 'Mummy is whispering to daddy'?

Once you have identified the children's language levels, you need to **expand on their message**. This will provide them with new words and help them to understand their experiences better. Try to add one or two more words to what children with speech and language delay have said.

For example, if the child says 'ball', then you could say, 'Yes, *big* ball'. Remember to emphasise the new vocabulary (pausing before the word and saying it slightly louder).

Other examples:

Child: 'more'
Adult response: 'more **bubbles**'

Child: 'apple'
Adult response: '**eating** apple'

Child: 'eating apple'
Adult response: '**Jake** eating apple'

Repeat

Children with speech and language delay need to hear the same words and phrases over and over again in a variety of situations and settings before they will remember and use them themselves. Aim to set up activities and events to expose the children to target words in fun and meaningful ways, for example:

Use the following sequence of responses while targeting words in the activities below:

1. First **carry out the activity once**, that is, posting one object, blowing bubbles once or feeding the child one mouthful.

2. Then **pause** for about two to three seconds while looking in anticipation at the child.

3. Next, **say and sign the gesture** for 'more' in an exaggerated way before carrying out the activity again or taking another turn.

4. **Continue with this**, encouraging the child to copy 'more' before you repeat the chosen activity.

Target words: 'farm animals', 'cow', 'pig' and 'sheep'

Activities:
- looking at books of farm animals
- doing animal puzzles
- playing with toy animals
- drawing/painting animals
- dressing up in animal costumes and acting out animal characters, while all the time labelling and pointing out the animals in a fun and meaningful way
- visiting a farm/zoo

Target word: 'more'

Activities:

- blowing bubbles
- playing with wind-up toys or ring-stackers
- posting toys, cards and objects
- playing anticipation games, such as 'Round and Round the Garden' and 'Peek-a-Boo'
- offering more food at meal and snack times

Target phrase: 'I want...'

Activities:

- doing puzzles
- dressing dollies and teddies
- playing shopping games
- reading books
- meal times

For example, ask for puzzle pieces using the carrier phrase 'I want...' (e.g. 'I want train/flower') while taking turns to build the puzzle. See if the child will take a turn in asking for a puzzle piece as well, without asking them to repeat back the target. Instead, wait for them to feel comfortable saying the phrase themselves. Often, children may need you to model the phrase several times before they will start using it.

Remember, children learn from hearing things over and over again in a meaningful and functional way during play and everyday activities, and not from being asked to repeat on demand.

Simplify

Imagine you are in a foreign country, when you only speak the local language at a basic level, and somebody starts asking you questions, assuming you are a competent speaker. It's unlikely that you will understand their requests. However, if they use gestures and only key words, that is, matching your language level, you are more likely to understand what they are saying. This is also the case for most children with speech and language delay. As an Early Years practitioner, your language needs to be at the level, or slightly higher than the level, that the child is at. For example, if the child is using single words, then your language input needs to be at the one- to two-word level: Use 'hat on' instead of 'Jimmy, we're going out. Put your hat on'. Say 'want biscuit' instead of 'Are you hungry? Do you want a biscuit?' Say 'eating apple' rather than 'Daddy's eating a nice green juicy apple'.

When you simplify your language, the children with speech and language delay are more likely to match the words with meaning.

Questions you might get asked

As Early Years Practitioners you are often the first person a parent might approach to discuss concerns about their child's development and communication skills. This section provides guidance on answering some of those questions.

Will baby signing help children to learn to talk?

Baby signing is a way of supplementing your talking by signing key words alongside your speech. The signs can be learnt through books, off the internet and through baby signing courses.

Baby signing has become fashionable in the UK amongst many parents and professionals in recent years. Joseph Garcia, an American scientist, when working as a signing interpreter for deaf parents, noticed that their hearing babies started communicating earlier than usual. In 1987, he started researching the effects of signing with hearing babies born to hearing parents. He found that if signed to regularly, these hearing babies started communicating at around 8-9 months old, earlier than those babies who were not exposed to sign. He later developed his own baby signing system to be used with hearing babies born to hearing parents. Since this time baby signing has been used worldwide.

Research has found that babies who were signed to from an early age understood and used more words and had better play skills. Parents also found that their babies were less frustrated, communicated more and there was a better bond between them and their babies. For more detail on this study see the article 'Developing language for life' at **www.literacytrust.org.uk.**

Some people believe that it is not the actual use of signing which is important in promoting early communication but rather the use of good interaction skills.

These include:

- the use of natural gesture alongside spoken language

- the use of good eye contact

- the use of facial expressions and body language

- watching the baby and responding to his/her interest.

- looking, listening and noting attempts to communicate and reinforcing these positively by copying, modelling and using natural gesture.

Contrary arguments suggest that there is no evidence that using baby signing will reduce frustration in normally developing babies, who are usually very good at making their needs known either vocally of non-vocally. Once again, refer to the above mentioned article at www.literacytrust.org.uk for more information.

In October 2003, a press release by *The Royal College of Speech and Language Therapists* stated that "a structured signing programme is not necessary to enhance the communication development of typically developing children" and that "The college is concerned that the use of signing does not replace/take priority over the need for parents to talk to their children". Good communication with children is the key to successful spoken language and talking to your baby is crucial. However for those children with additional needs, such as Down's syndrome, the use of baby signing and natural gesture is beneficial. Visit **www.rcslt.co.uk** for more information.

Is it possible for a child to learn two languages together?

Learning more than one language at a time does not necessarily mean that one or both languages will be delayed or develop at a slower rate.

Broadly speaking, those children who are exposed to two languages before the age of 3 years, in roughly equal amounts, should acquire fluency in both languages at a rate comparable to peers who are learning one language (Padilla and Liebman 1975). More current research is finding that if a child acquires two languages simultaneously the stages of development are the same as for those children learning one language. There is a debate over whether learning two languages simultaneously results in a slower rate of vocabulary development. Goodz (1994) reports no delay in vocabulary development, whereas other researchers e.g. Bialystok (1998) report lower rates of vocabulary development in those children learning two languages when compared to those learning one.

The key to ensuring good language acquisition in both languages is:

- Being consistent with when and where the two languages are used. For example, if English is spoken at the early years setting, it should not be mixed with any additional languages. For children whose first language is not used in the early years setting, it is worth suggesting to parents that they also stick to one language only – be it English or their mother tongue. For example, if the mother/father decides to speak to their child in Punjabi, then it is important that they don't mix it with English. Alternatively, some family members may decide to use English with the child – once again it is important that they don't mix the two languages. The child will begin to associate the language to the person and/or setting where it is used.

- Using a good language model. If a child is exposed to an inaccurate and/or inconsistent language model, then they are likely to be delayed in learning language in terms of vocabulary and grammatical structure. For example, in some languages, there is no distinction between the use of 'he' versus 'she'. The parent may therefore use these pronouns interchangeably in English to refer to either a man/boy or woman/girl.

In a study by Grosjean in 1982, it was found that children who are exposed to two languages, simultaneously in equal amounts tended to:

- Initially mix the languages, then slowly separate them and become increasingly aware of their differences.
- Use the language associated with the specific environment.
- Avoid difficult words and grammatical structures in the weaker language.
- Develop fluency in both languages, however still favour one.

For those children who are exposed to a second language after the age of 3 years, such as those who learn English only at their early years setting, fluency is less predictable. If the first language is well developed before entering the early years setting it may be that learning the second language is hindered by the development of the first. Alternatively, the introduction of a second language may be facilitated by already having an existing language. Success in the acquisition of the languages is not thought to be dependent upon intelligence but rather the desire to communicate and the environment.

And finally, it is usual for both adults and children to switch between languages, commonly known as 'code switching'. This may happen for a variety of reasons, such as the speaker favouring a specific word or grammatical structure, wanting to add emphasis to what was said or not having a translatable word available.

The National Association for Language Development in the Curriculum (**www.naldic.org.uk**) can provide early years practitioners with guidance and information on supporting bilingual/multilingual children in the EYFS. You can also visit **www.iteachilearn.com** for articles and information on bilingualism and the teaching of EAL (English as an Additional Language) learners.

What happens when a child from the early years setting is referred to a speech and language therapist?

The child and their parents/carer will be invited for an initial consultation with the speech and language therapist. The parents/carer will have the opportunity to discuss the referral letter and their concerns as well as concerns raised by the early years practitioners involved with the child. It will be useful for both parties to discuss their views of the child's speech and language development before they attend the consultation. The therapist will probably ask the parents questions about their child's development and family set up. They may also request information from the early years practitioners if consent is granted by the parents/carer. This can take the form of a telephone conversation or the therapist visiting the early years provision to observe the child. The information you provide will help the therapist to identify any difficulties, understand the child better and provide appropriate intervention.

You can suggest to parents/carer that they write down when their child reached certain developmental milestones as part of the information gathering process. For example when did the child:

- start sitting
- start crawling
- start standing and walking
- start babbling
- start saying single words
- start joining words together
- become toilet trained during the day and night
- start feeding themselves independently
- start dressing themselves independently
- start responding to their name
- start understanding simple instructions?

You may also want to think about:

- How the child communicates and makes his/her wants, needs and desires known?
- How does he/she interact with others?
- What does he/she like to play with?
- How many words does he/she understand?
- How many words does he/she use?
- How many words does he/she join together?

It is useful to provide parents with early years provision reports which they can take to the consultation along with any other relevant letters, hearing test results and medical reports.

Following on from this, the therapist will assess the child by observing them playing either alone or with parents/carer. They will look at the child's:

- attention and listening skills
- turn-taking skills
- eye contact
- play skills
- understanding of words/signs and instructions
- memory of spoken words

- expressive language i.e. the words, signs or gestures that he/she uses and how they join them together

- how he/she uses language

- the clarity of his/her speech

- problem solving skills

The therapist might use a variety of formal and/or informal assessments and activities to gather this information. Formal testing often involves labeling and/or identifying pictures or objects.

Once the therapist has obtained all the necessary information, the outcomes will be discussed with the parent and, with consent, a report will be circulated to the relevant professionals. The report will include assessment results and recommendations.

The assessment may show that the child's speech and language skills are within the normal age range and therefore do not require therapy. Alternatively it may be recommended that;

- The child has one to one therapy, focusing on specific therapy aims. The frequency of the sessions will depend on the child's needs and the local service.

- The child has group therapy, whereby the child's speech and language needs will be addressed in a group of children with similar difficulties.

- The child has review sessions to monitor their progress.

- The parents/carer are trained in using 'parent-child interaction' strategies.

- The speech and language therapist attends the early years provision to support practitioners in their work with the child.

- The child follows a specific targeted home/school programme.

Parents and early years practitioners are encouraged to take an active part in the therapy process by carrying out a home/school programme. This is essential for the child, to help them achieve and generalise their goals. Therapy sessions may take place at the child's home, in the local clinic or in the early years provision. This will depend on the local service policy. The key person involved with the child will be encouraged to attend therapy sessions if they take place in the early years provision.

Do early years practitioners work with the speech and language therapist?

Speech and language therapists may visit early years settings or require the child to attend a clinic. Your local service will have a policy governing where children are seen.

If the child is to be seen in the early years provision, the parents' permission will always be sought prior to any contact and the parent will be encouraged to attend.

Speech and language therapists aim to work closely with early years practitioners in a number of possible ways, these may include:

- sending assessment reports to the early years setting (with parents' permission)
- telephoning early years practitioners to discuss the child and provide tips and strategies
- sending work to the early years provision
- supporting early years practitioners in specific areas of communication
- observing the child in the early years provision.

Early years practitioners are pivotal in supporting children with speech and language delay and guiding them through the EYFS curriculum. They also play a critical role in supporting and empowering parents of children with speech and language delay in developing their communication skills and confidence as social communicators.

"We consider the parent partnership to be a crucial part of providing effective teaching and therapy for your child within a warm and trusting environment" and "We invite you the parent to be a keen and enthusiastic contributor to the team approach" (Christopher Place -The Speech, Language and Hearing Centre, 2009).

Developing key skills and understanding learning styles

As an Early Years practitioner/key worker, you have the greatest opportunity to gain detailed knowledge of individual children's strengths and abilities, as well as their areas of difficulty. You know their interests and what motivates them, which is really important for devising activities to develop their language.

When aiming to develop key skills in children with speech and language delay, it's also important to identify their learning styles and schemas through careful observation. Your planning should take this into consideration as it will enable you to engage the child's attention and facilitate their learning.

Learning styles

Children learn in different ways. For some, learning may be enhanced by:

- The use of **visual cues** such as pictures, symbols, signs and gestures. These children are commonly referred to as 'visual learners'. They often struggle when information is spoken to them without the support of pictures and gestures.

- The use of **sensory cues**. This might include the use of sand, water, shaving foam and so on. These children are commonly referred to as 'tactile learners'.

- **Experiencing actions and events first hand**. They need to carry out the action before they truly understand it, such as visiting the zoo, growing seeds or hatching eggs. They often struggle when information is spoken to them without experiencing it.

In the Early Years it is good to supply the group with activities that encompass different types of learning styles.

Schemas

'Schemas are patterns of linked behaviors, which the child can generalise and use in a whole variety of different situations.' (Bruce,1997).

Children generally use one or more schemas in a variety of contexts and activities, such as outside play, the home corner and child-initiated play.

Possible schemas might include:

- Transporting, where the children carry things from one point to another e.g. they may carry animals from one place to another in a box or sand from the sand pit to the home corner in a bucket.

- Enveloping, where the children cover themselves and objects. For example, they may cover teddy up in a blanket or wrap pencils in a cloth.

- Rotation, where the children are fascinated by spinning and rotating objects e.g. they may like to watch the wheels go round on a car or enjoy rolling down a hill.

There are many different types of schema. For more information, refer to Key Times – A Framework for Developing High Quality Provision for Children Under Three Years Old, Manning-Morton, J,. and Thorp, M. (2001). See also *Again, Again* by Stella Louis, *Featherstone Education*.

Early Years practitioners should observe and identify children's schemas and plan activities accordingly.

Special time

In busy Early Years settings, it is often difficult to find a significant amount of quality time or space to focus on one child's needs. This is why we suggest you ask parents to set aside five to ten minutes of 'special time', several times a week, spending uninterrupted, individual quality time with their child.

'Special time' needs to be at a time when the child is not tired, hungry or upset. It needs to be in a quiet environment in which the television or radio is turned off and other possible distractions removed. Parents can select three to five interesting activities for each special time. They should place the activities in a bag or box and bring them out one at a time. Parents should avoid having too many toys on the table or floor at a time as this might be distracting to their child. Once an activity is finished, they should return it to the bag or box.

Some of the advantages of 'special time' are:

- It's short, which means that parents can fit it into their daily schedule.

- It's regular, which means that parents can also repeat and reinforce language activities and practise the 'The Rapper's Way' (see page 33).

- It's at a specified time, which means that the child can look forward to one-to-one time with a parent

This is also a chance for parents to relax, enjoy their child and encourage language development through fun play. As an Early Years practitioner or key person, your role is to inspire and support parents.

Speech and language foundation skills

Children with speech and language delay often have difficulties in some or all of the following areas:

- Listening
- Attention
- Turn-taking
- Eye contact
- Play

Listening

The ability to listen is a fundamental skill that all children need to acquire in order to understand and use language, and develop their social skills. Children with speech and language delay may often present with many difficulties developing their listening skills. They therefore tend to benefit from participating in adult-directed activities and games that will enhance this area of their development.

Activities need to be aimed at the children's level of listening and taken to the next stage. The following activities can be varied to suit the children's interests and keep them motivated.

Activities to develop listening skills:

- **Listening walks**

Encourage the children to stop and listen to the sounds around them, such as the washing machine, the doorbell, the phone, water being poured, a dog barking, an aeroplane and a kettle whistling. Make them aware of the sounds around them by pointing to your ear and, where possible, go to the source of the sound and label it. For example, when you hear an aeroplane, point to your ear and then towards the plane, encouraging the children to look at the plane while saying 'plane'.

- **Ready, Steady, Go games**

These games can be played in a variety of settings with a variety of toys, waiting for **'GO'** before:

- going down a slide
- running between two points
- kicking a ball
- placing a shape in a shape sorter
- knocking down towers or skittles
- dropping toy animals in sand or water
- opening a jack-in-the-box
- activating a musical toy.

Initially, you may need to demonstrate the activity and use gesture to prompt for waiting and 'GO'.

- **Experimenting with sound makers and musical instruments**

Put objects such as rice, pasta, stones and beads in metal or plastic containers and encourage the children to shake, roll, drop and play with them. Encourage the children to shake them loudly, quietly, fast and slow while listening to the sound they make.

- **Shopping game**

Place five or six familiar objects on a table and supply the children with a shopping bag before giving them instructions to select one or a number of items to place in the bag. This game can be varied to include putting clothes on a washing line or removing them.

- **Singing familiar nursery rhymes**

For more advanced children, you can miss out and/or substitute predictable words, and encourage them to fill in or correct the script, for example: 'Incy Wincy spider went up the watering can' – then encourage the child to detect your mistake and correct it. 'Twinkle, twinkle, little star, how I wonder what you_____' – then pause and encourage the child to finish the end of the rhyme.

- **Listening group game**

With children sitting in a circle, you can ask them to identify those with specific characteristics, for example, 'Who's wearing a pink t-shirt?', 'Find a person with short hair', 'Find boys wearing blue jumpers/black shoes' etc. Use vocabulary that the children know.

Attention

A child's ability to listen progresses at different developmental levels and stages. For more information on the normal stages of attention development, refer to *The Cooper-Moodley Stages of Attention Control* (Cooper, J., Moodley, M. and Reynell, J. (1978) Helping Language Development, Edward Arnold Ltd).

It is important that children can share attention on an activity or object that another person draws their attention to. This is called joint attention and is a crucial part of language development and usually starts being established early on in the child's life. It is essential that the child acquires joint attention to enable them to learn language and take part in conversations.

To support the development of attention, it is essential that you remove all possible distractions, for example, additional toys/people.

Activities to develop attention skills:

- **Surprise feely bag**

Place interesting objects in a brightly coloured bag or sparkly box. Create anticipation about what is in the bag or box. Invite the children to select one item from the bag or box and then, with the child, explore and play with the item. Select interesting items to put in the bag or box, such as play dough, squeezy balls, massagers, wind-up toys, musical toys and toys that light up. Once you have finished exploring a toy, remove it from sight before the children select more toys.

- **Bubbles**

Blow bubbles with the children, watch them go up and down, and pop and catch them. As a variation, you can also blow up balloons, let them go and watch them spin around the room.

- **Exploring new ways to play with the same toy**

Children's attention can be extended by playing with toys in different ways, for example, by:

- fitting puzzle pieces one at a time and then asking the child to post specific puzzle pieces

- undressing a dolly, pretending to wash the clothes and then hanging them on a line

- playing with animals, washing them, feeding them, hiding them in sand, sorting them into different categories and matching animal sounds to toy animals and/or pictures

- playing with cars while showing how cars and trailers can be linked up, raced and bumped together.

Remember that your language level needs to be appropriate for the child with speech and language delay.

- **What's different?**

Encourage the children to sit in a circle. Then invite one child to stand up while the remaining children observe what he or she is wearing. The selected child should then leave the room. Whilst out of sight, the child changes one item of their clothing, for example, taking off their shoe and putting on a Wellington boot, putting up their shirt collar, rolling up their sleeves or turning their jumper round. The child then re-enters the room while the other children have to identify what is different about the child.

Remember that many of the games described for one specific area of communication will also help to develop other communication skills.

Turn-taking

Turn-taking is an essential part of conversation – knowing when to listen and when to talk. Often, children with speech and language difficulties have delayed turn-taking skills.

The following activities aim to develop turn-taking in a very real way:

- Take turns with a child to put pieces in a puzzle or shape sorter. Prompt the child to wait and take their turn.

- Take turns to post or throw objects in a post box/bin/empty box.

- Take turns to remove exciting objects from a bag or box.

- Pass or roll a ball, bean bag or microphone around a group of children.
  This activity can be made verbal by children answering questions or sharing information only when they have the object.

The games can be made more difficult by increasing the number of people involved and the language complexity.

Most games and activities that involve more than one person can be adapted to practise turn-taking.

Eye contact

Appropriate eye contact is another important component of social interaction. If children have difficulties in this area, they might use eye contact on their own terms, for example, only when they want something. Alternatively, eye contact may be fleeting or the child may stare intensely at people.

Activities to develop eye contact:

- Use a silly hat, nose, mask or funny make-up to encourage the children to look at you. Reward good eye contact with a smile or phrase such as 'great looking!'
- Say a child's name and wait for a response. Say it again. If they are still not looking, gently turn their heads towards you. Reward eye contact with a smile. It is, vital that you reward every attempt. If children respond to their name and you don't reward the response appropriately, they will soon learn to ignore it again. Slowly reduce the amount of physical prompting but always maintain the reward.
- Encourage the children to sit in a circle. The Early Years practitioner then stands in the middle of the circle and winks at a child. The children in the circle need to look at the practitioner to see if they are winked at. The child who is winked at then stands in the middle and becomes the 'winker'.

Play

By developing play, children learn more about their environment and world; they develop language and learn how to interact socially. Language develops in well-defined stages (see pages 70 – 75). Our aim here is to provide you with ideas and activities for the main stages of play development.

Exploratory play

In exploratory play, children use their different senses to explore the environment and find out how things work. Your role should be to extend and guide their play.

Activities to encourage exploratory play:

- Encouraging children to explore a variety of textures, consistencies, sounds and smells (e.g. playing with sand/water/play dough)
- Using a 'treasure basket' for children to explore different items. This can be created by putting interesting everyday objects, such as a brush, duster, wooden spoon and cup in a basket, box or bag and encouraging the children to explore the objects. Elinor Goldschmied developed the concept of treasure baskets, which are widely used in Early Years settings to help babies and young children to explore (Goldschmied, E., 1989).

Cause and effect

Cause and effect activities involve carrying out an action and expecting a consistent response. This is the foundation for children learning that their actions have a consequence or impact on their environment, eventually leading to the knowledge that their words have the power to influence those around them.

Activities to encourage cause and effect:

- Pressing a button and hearing a sound.

- Opening a box and a frog jumps out.

- Banging instruments together to make a noise.

- Playing games where the children learn to anticipate an action, such as playing Peek-a-Boo, Round and Round the Garden, Jack-in-the-Box and Waiting for a Tickle.

There are many commercial products available, for example, hammering a ball through a hole and jumping on a mat to make a sound.

Symbolic play

Symbolic play involves interacting with toys or real objects in a meaningful way. As children's play develops, they should start to use common objects appropriately on themselves, others (including peers and adults) and teddies and dollies. When developing start with large objects and, as the child becomes more familiar with the play, decrease the size of the toys, for example, move from large dolls to small play figures. Try to use a variety of play scenarios to develop the child's understanding of different situations.

Activities to encourage symbolic play:

- Involve children in everyday activities, such as washing, feeding and dressing a baby or doll, wiping the table and washing the dishes. Use simple language to accompany your actions, for example, 'baby drinking', 'baby eating', 'washing baby' and so on.

- Use large play objects to act out familiar scenes, such as doctors and nurses, picnics and cooking. Model actions and sequences while using simple language to accompany your play. For example, in domestic play and cooking, encourage the children to pretend to cook food, dish it out and eat it.

- Act out familiar traditional stories, such as 'Three Little Pigs' and 'Little Red Riding Hood' while dressing up and encouraging the children to take on different roles.

- Use small play people and accessories to act out different play scenarios, such as farm scenes, zoo and play park scenes.

Imaginative play

Imaginative play, often referred to as make-believe play, is important for the development of abstract thinking. It allows children to explore new roles and express emotions, and it encourages creativity.

Activities to encourage imaginative play:

- Have a bag filled with versatile objects, such as a block of wood, cotton reels threaded on a piece of string, a piece of material and a pencil. Encourage the children to think how they can use the objects in play, for example, a block of wood can be used as an ice-lolly, a telephone or an animal. The cotton reels could be used as a snake or a necklace. A bowl could be used as a hat, an egg box as a boat, and a pencil as a guitar.

- Encourage the children to act out different make-believe characters, such as fairies, astronauts, pirates, princes and princesses.

How to engage the child with speech and language delay in these play activities:

- Choose motivating play materials to gain the child's attention.

- Position yourself opposite the child for the duration of the activity so that you can effectively model the play.

- Provide demonstrations of how to use and extend different objects and materials in a meaningful way, for example, encourage the child to look at you while you pretend to brush your own hair, then the hair of a doll, before offering the brush to the child, encouraging them to copy your actions.

- Provide simple language, at the level of the child, to accompany play actions.

- Remember to use praise, rewards and prompts to encourage the child to participate.

Receptive language

The understanding of language begins at birth. Before children are able to understand real words and sentences, they need to develop an understanding of their environment. This is known as situational understanding. Examples of situational understanding include a baby knowing that they will be fed when the parent approaches with a spoon, or a toddler knowing that when they see the car keys or dog lead, they need to get their coat to go outside. The child does not necessarily understand the words but rather what the objects represent.

Gradually, children will begin to understand frequently used words that represent objects and actions. For the child to grasp a true understanding of the words, they need to hear them in a variety of settings. As children's understanding develops, they will be able to understand longer and more complex instructions.

To understand an instruction or comment, children need to understand the words, the grammatical concepts (e.g. location vocabulary such as 'in', 'on' and 'under', who's doing what to whom, and pronouns such as 'you', 'me', 'she', 'he' and 'they') and the key elements of the sentence. For example, for a comment such as 'Give Ben the teddy', the child has to:

- understand all the vocabulary (e.g. give, Ben and teddy),

- know that the teddy has to go to Ben and not the other way around,

- remember that the teddy needs to be given to Ben as opposed to just picking up the teddy.

As sentences grow in complexity, children will have to remember and understand more information. By developing the key areas of vocabulary, early concepts, grammatical structures and auditory memory, you can aim to extend the children's language understanding.

Developing situational understanding of everyday routines

- Select items to represent specific activities, that is, objects of reference, for example, a spoon for lunch time, a musical instrument for circle time and a toy potty for going to the toilet. These items should be used regularly and consistently to refer to specific activities. This can be done by showing the child the object and labelling the activity it refers to before starting the task. For further information on the use of objects of reference, consult your local speech and language therapist.

- Use photos and symbols of objects and activities, such as a photo or symbol of paint brushes to represent painting and a photo or symbol of a book to represent story time. For further advice and materials needed to implement and extend the use of photos and symbols, also liaise with your local speech and language therapist.

Developing vocabulary

Repetition is key when learning new words. Children need to hear new words in a variety of contexts and sentence structures to gain a full understanding. Using speech accompanied by gesture, pointing and sign will help a child to learn new words.

Please note that any reference to signing refers to Makaton signing and not to British Sign Language. In the Makaton signing system, core vocabulary is signed with speech. For further information, see **www.makaton.co.uk**.

When teaching new vocabulary, the new words should be stressed and positioned at the end of the sentence or phrase. The rest of the information in the phrase should be redundant or familiar vocabulary so that the child can focus on the new word.

Activities to develop vocabulary:

- Label objects and actions of interest in the child's surroundings and view, such as food items, clothing, toys and actions. Talk about the functions and attributes of items, such as size, colour or texture, and to what category they belong, for example, zoo animals, furniture, things you eat and so on. Target words that are appropriate and suitable for your child.

- Label objects, emotions and actions of interest in books.

- Play as described in the play activities.

- Play lotto matching games.

- Play fishing games (paper clips can be attached to pictures and a rod made by using a stick and a magnet). Encourage the children to 'fish' picture cards and label them.

- Make scrapbooks with pictures or photos of objects and actions that are interesting to the child. Label and talk about what people are doing and how they are feeling in the pictures.

- Play a 'What's in the Box?' game (place a selection of objects in an interesting box and encourage the child to knock on the box, open it and select an object). You can then label the objects that the child selects.

- Play musical 'listen and do'. Play music and encourage the child to move around the room. When the music stops, give them an instruction, such as 'jump up and down', 'go to sleep' and 'hop' etc. Encourage the child to carry out the action.

- Play traditional games such as 'Simon Says'.

- Partially hide objects around a room and encourage the child to search for specific items.

- Play positional hide and seek. The adult hides common objects in positions around the room and then gives the child an instruction, such as 'Look under the flower pot'. Initially, you may wish to use gesture to accompany your voice to indicate the position. The child then goes to look for the object.

- It might be helpful to send a list of topic vocabulary home for parents to include in games and chat at home.

- It might also be helpful to write unfamiliar vocabulary in the Early Years setting home book to encourage the parent and Early Years practitioner to reinforce it.

Remember that the more the child hears the words in a variety of settings, the more they are likely to understand the meaning of the words.

Understanding grammatical structures

There are many grammatical structures that we learn as our language develops. In this section, we aim to give you ideas on how to facilitate the understanding of some of the more basic language structures.

Possessives

This refers to words and word endings that indicate who something belongs to, for example 'Mummy's bag', and early possessive pronouns, such as '**mine**' and '**yours**'.

Activities to develop the understanding of possessives:

- At circle time, take it in turns to point to parts of a puppet or a dolly while emphasising the possessives, for example, ask the child to point to '*doll's* hand'.

Here is **your** bag

- At home time, when giving children their possessions back, such as their bags and coats, label who they belong to, for example, 'It's *yours*' and 'That's *Jimmy's* bag'.

- Encourage the children to bring in personal items, such as toys. Place them in a bag. At circle time, place the box in the centre of the carpet and invite children one at a time to the box. The Early Years practitioner should instruct the child to whom to give the toy. For example, tell the child 'It's *Bob's* bus' while encouraging them to give it to Bob.

Pronouns

Pronouns refer to words such as 'I', 'he', 'she', 'we', 'you', 'they', 'him' and 'her' and are substitutes for people's names.

Activities to develop the understanding of pronouns:

- Sort pictures into boy and girl categories. Introduce the labels 'he' and 'she'.

- Label and describe pictures using the name/gender of the person. Slowly substitute the name or gender for 'he' and 'she' (e.g. The boy is eating an apple. Look, **he**'s eating an apple). Be sure to emphasise the pronoun.

- Play a sticker game. Have two sets of pictures, one of a boy doing an action and one of a girl doing the same action, such as a boy/girl eating an apple, boy/girl brushing their teeth and boy/girl washing a car. Tell the child to close their eyes whilst you are hiding a sticker under one of the pictures. Then let the child open their eyes. Without pointing, tell the child where the sticker is hidden, emphasising the pronoun (e.g. '**He** is eating an apple').

- 'Mine' and 'yours' can be targeted in turn-taking games, such as blowing bubbles and throwing balls. Model and encourage the child to use 'my turn' and 'your turn'.

Tenses

It has long been recognised that children first need to understand that actions and events occur in a sequential order before they can begin to understand the concept of time (Cole, 1982). It is therefore important for children to develop the ability to sequence events and stories. Once this skill is established, children can begin to understand and use simple tenses to refer to events in the past, present and future.

Activities to develop sequencing and understanding of tenses:

- Using simple language, talk about how we carry out daily routines using sequencing words such as 'first', 'then' or 'next', and 'lastly', for example, for brushing your teeth: '*first* you squeeze the toothpaste onto the toothbrush, *then* you brush your teeth, and *lastly* you rinse the toothbrush'. For pouring a drink: '*first* you get the cup, *then* you pour the juice, and *then* you drink the juice'.

- Cut out or draw pictures of familiar routines such as those described previously, and encourage the child to order and describe them.

- Tell the child stories using the words 'first', 'next' and 'lastly'.

- Keep a picture diary with the child and talk about what they did yesterday and/or what they will do tomorrow.

- At the end of the day, encourage the children to talk about what they have done and what they will do later that evening. Where necessary, the adult should model the correct tense, for example, 'Today, I *painted* a picture' or 'This afternoon, I am *going* to Sam's house'.

Plurals

Plurals refer to the concept of more than one, such as 'you have six apples' as opposed to the singular (one apple). For regular plurals, there is an additional sound placed on the end of the noun. However, in English, there are many irregular plurals that need to be taught separately. For example, the plural of 'sheep' is 'sheep'. The plural of 'man' is 'men'.

Activities to develop plurals:

- Play shopping style games where you request one or more items to buy, for example, 'Can I have the apples?' and 'I would like the carrot'. Be sure not to use the number of items you want. Use 'an/a', such as 'a banana', as this will give the child an additional cue. As before, highlight the final 's' to aid the child's understanding.

- Plural lotto games whereby the children have to match single nouns with their corresponding regular plurals. For example, matching a picture of a teddy with a picture of teddies. The Early Years practitioner should model this, emphasising the plural(s). This type of game can be made using photos and pictures cut from magazines.

Auditory memory

Auditory memory is the ability to remember key verbal elements in an instruction or command. A child with poor auditory memory may understand all the vocabulary and grammatical structures, but still not successfully complete the task. Auditory memory should not be confused with visual memory, as a child may remember seeing places and events in the past, and could be using visual strength and not actually remembering auditory information.

To develop auditory memory, you can:

- Place six objects on the table and give the child the instruction to get one, two or three objects and put them in a shopping bag. A similar version can be done for posting pictures in a box.

- When out shopping with a child, ask them to go and get items.

- When unpacking boxes, give the child instructions to put objects in specific locations, for example, 'Put the paint on the table'.

- Place familiar items of clothes on a washing line and ask the child to fetch one, two or three items.

Ensure that you give the instructions as one complete phrase and do not break it up into its separate elements. Remember the vocabulary must be familiar as the aim is not to teach new vocabulary, but rather expand the child's auditory memory.

Expressive language

Expressive language refers to the way a person expresses themselves: communicating wants, needs and interests. This may take the form of gurgling, smiling, babbling, crying, playing and pointing in a baby or, as in an adult, more complex verbal and non-verbal exchanges. In a typically developing child, expressive language develops in well-defined stages as set out on pages 72 – 75.

Usually, receptive language develops prior to expressive language. We therefore expect a typically developing child to understand a word or concept before using it. However, communication would be unnatural if we were to target one without the other.

The activities outlined in this section go hand-in-hand with those in the preceding section, 'Understanding of language'. We have separated them for clarity.

Meaningful sounds and early words

A child's first words are usually meaningful play sounds ('brumm-brumm', 'moo' and so on) and approximations for words that they hear frequently, such as 'mummy', 'daddy', 'drink', 'No!' and 'bye bye', often repeated from an adult model and accompanied by a waving gesture.

Activities to develop play sounds:

- Model and encourage representational sounds during play and everyday situations.

- Engage the child in action rhyme songs, such as 'Old Macdonald' and 'Wheels on the Bus', which incorporate many representational sounds.

- Model and encourage the child to use simple functional high frequency words such as 'more', 'again', 'bye bye' and 'go'. This can be targeted in a range of activities and everyday situations, such as:

  o blowing bubbles and encouraging the child to request more before another turn.

  o winding up a wind-up toy, and modelling and encouraging the child to say 'again'.

  o giving the child a puzzle piece one at a time, modelling and encouraging the child to ask for more before giving the next piece – once the puzzle is complete, you can model and encourage the child to say 'bye bye' to pieces one at a time before throwing them into a bucket or posting them in a letter box.

  o modelling and encouraging the child to ask for 'more' before being given more juice or food at meal times and snack times.

  o offering the child two choices for which they have to verbalise a preference, such as 'Do you want water or juice?' at meal times and snack times.

  o playing ready-steady-go games. For example, modelling and encouraging 'go' before throwing a beanbag into a bucket, going down a slide or opening a jack-in-the-box.

- modelling and encouraging the child to label objects and actions. This can be targeted whilst:

  - looking at books

  - playing with toys

  - building puzzles

  - out shopping

  - cooking

  - visiting a farm/zoo

  - getting dressed

  - drawing on an interactive whiteboard

  - encouraging the children to take pictures with cameras and labelling the images. Vocabulary books can also be made with the photos.

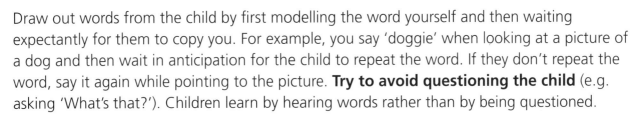

Draw out words from the child by first modelling the word yourself and then waiting expectantly for them to copy you. For example, you say 'doggie' when looking at a picture of a dog and then wait in anticipation for the child to repeat the word. If they don't repeat the word, say it again while pointing to the picture. **Try to avoid questioning the child** (e.g. asking 'What's that?'). Children learn by hearing words rather than by being questioned.

Joining words

Many of the activities listed earlier can also be used to encourage children to use two- or three-word phrases. As a general rule, encourage the child to use longer utterances by adding a word to the phrase. If the child says 'doggie' whilst looking at a picture of a dog sleeping, you can extend the phrase by adding a word, for example, 'doggie's sleeping', while emphasising the new word. In time, the child should begin to use the new phrase. A similar approach can be used when trying to extend the child's language from a two-word phrase to a three word phrase.

It is important to be mindful of children who consistently repeat words but appear not to understand their meaning. This pattern of repetition of speech and language is referred is to as echolalia.

More ideas and activities to develop expressive language:

- When tidying up toys, model and encourage 'in the box' whilst putting objects in the box.

- While acting out real-life events with toys, such as washing up, bathing and shopping, model and encourage the child to describe what is happening, for example, 'washing cup', 'washing baby's ears' and 'want apple'.

- At snack time, if the child requests 'more' to indicate wanting more biscuit, model and encourage the child to label what they want more of, for example, 'more biscuit', 'more juice' and 'more bubbles'.

- While playing fishing type games, as described earlier where paper clips are attached to pictures and a magnet is attached to a piece of string, help children to fish for and label the pictures. Once again, model it and encourage the child to extend their phrases. For example, when the child says 'Baby sleeping', you can say 'Baby's sleeping **in a bed**', stressing the new words.

It is important to remember to only extend the child's language by one word, for example, if the child is regularly using two-word phrases, model three words. Additionally, remember children learn through hearing words and phrases. Try to avoid asking the child to repeat what you said and/or asking too many questions.

Helping with grammar

Remember that for children to use grammatical structures correctly in their speech, they must first understand the concepts. It may be useful to carry out these expressive language tasks alongside the receptive tasks (see page 55).

Pronouns
Pronouns refer to words such as 'I', 'he', 'she', 'we', 'you', 'they', 'him' and 'her'.

Activities to develop expressive use of pronouns:
- Encourage the children to label pictures of boys and girls performing different actions by using the sentence structure 'He/she is…'.
- During play activities, use small people figures of boys and girls, mummies and daddies, and encourage the children to carry out and label actions with the figures. For example, when putting a girl to bed, encourage the child to say 'She is sleeping'.

Tenses
Tenses are often a difficult concept for children with speech and language delay to grasp. Using sequencing activities and words such as 'first', 'next' and 'last' as well as such words as 'yesterday', 'today', 'tomorrow', 'now' and 'later' will help to facilitate children's understanding and use of different tenses.

Activities to develop sequencing and the use of tenses:
- Encourage the children to tell their news to other members of the group. Home books can be used to prompt the children about what they have done or are going to do.
- At the end of the session, encourage the children to talk about what they have done and what they will do later that evening. Where necessary, the adult should model the correct tense. For example, 'Today I **painted** a picture' and 'Tonight, I am **going** to Sam's house'.

Negatives
At the simplest level, negative concepts refer to 'no!', 'don't!' and 'not!'. At the more advanced level, negative concepts may include sentences containing 'neither/nor', 'hasn't got' and so on.

Activities to develop the expressive use of negatives:
- Play with a puppet and encourage the children to answer 'yes/no' questions, for example, 'Does monkey have a tail?' The child then says 'yes'. 'Does monkey have earrings?' The child then says 'no' etc.

- Encourage the children to talk about, and listen to, their peers' likes and dislikes e.g. 'I like chocolate but I don't like vegetables'.

- Place a selection of pictures or photos on a table and encourage the children to match the picture to your negative verbal description. For example, you could say 'the man is **not** drinking' and then ask the children to scan the pictures and select the correct one matching the specific description. Initially, you may need to prompt with a nod or head shake and emphasise the negative words to aid the child's understanding and use of them.

- Encourage the children to sit in a circle. Then use a negative sentence construction to describe one of the children in the class and ask the others to identify who that child is, for example, 'Who **hasn't** got a hat on?'

Plurals

For regular plurals, there is an additional 's' sound placed on the end of the noun. However, in English, there are many irregular plurals that need to be taught separately. The plural of 'man' is 'men'. The plural of 'child' is 'children' and so on.

Remember that for a child to use plurals correctly in their speech, they must first understand the concept of more than one. It may be useful to carry out these expressive language tasks alongside the receptive tasks.

Activities to develop plurals:

- Play shopping-type games and encourage the child to request one or more items to buy, for example, 'Can I have the books?' or 'I would like the dog'.

- Play plural lotto games whereby children have to match single nouns with their corresponding regular plurals, for example, matching a picture of a teddy with a picture of teddies. Encourage the children to label the pictures they use. If necessary, model the game, emphasising the plural 's'. This type of game can be made using photos and pictures cut from magazines.

Functional language

Functional language refers to using language purposefully between adults and peers. It involves an element of understanding and processing what is happening in the scenario or event, identifying and planning a response, and communicating the message in an appropriate and meaningful way.

For example, during snack time, a child may not have a cup for juice. The child needs to understand the situation (i.e. snack time), identify what they require – the cup – and formulate an appropriate request to the right person.

Children with speech and language delay may struggle with any part of this. This can lead to the child feeling frustrated and that their needs and interests are not understood.

The following are all aspects of functional language that you can target in the Early Years provision.

Commenting

Commenting refers to a child's ability to label objects, actions, feelings and experiences, and to report actions and events in a meaningful way. Commenting is one of the foundations of communication and social interaction. It enables us to empathise and share interests, information and experiences, and form meaningful relationships with others.

This can be targeted in the Early Years provision by providing appropriate vocabulary to reflect the child's thoughts, interests and feelings, for example, saying 'wet-wet-wet' when the child shows interest in splashing their hands in a water tray and 'Mmm, Molly's eating' when the child is having a snack.

Requesting and questioning

It is important to be aware of the difference between yes/no or closed questions and open-ended questions. The former require a simple yes/no answer while the latter requires a more complex explanation.

Questions can be formulated around **where, when, who, what, why and how**. Refer to pages 70 – 75 for more information about when children should acquire understanding and use of these question forms. For the purpose of this section, we aim to give you general advice on developing children's abilities to ask questions and make requests.

- Children could take it in turns to pretend to be different animals while you encourage the other children to ask questions such as 'Are you a lion/monkey?', 'Do you live in a zoo? and 'Do you like bananas?,' and the child should respond with yes/no answers. This can be modelled with another adult when necessary.

- At snack time, give the children the opportunity to ask their peers what they would like to drink or eat, or perhaps what colour cup they want. Initially, you may need to model the question format, for example, 'What colour cup?' and 'Do you want apple or orange?'.

- During circle time, encourage the children to ask a puppet, dolly or teddy simple questions, such as 'What is your name?' and 'How old are you?'

- Use everyday activities, such as snack time and play time, to encourage the children to request objects, such as 'Want cup' at snack time, 'Open' to open a packet of dried fruit or 'I would like the yellow paint'.

Reasoning and problem solving

Reasoning and problem solving refer to the ability to analyse and identify potential obscurities and difficulties, and to work out a solution. For example, if it is raining outside, the child needs to identify the potential problem of getting wet when going outside and coming up with a solution, such as using an umbrella or a rain coat. This is an important element of functional language and an integral part of everyday life. It is important to start developing these skills at an early age. Children with speech and language delay often find these skills difficult to master as they are more abstract and less concrete than other elements of language.

Activities to help develop reasoning and problem solving:

- Encourage the children to sit in a circle. One child goes out of the room and changes their appearance to create an absurdity. For example, removing one shoe, putting shorts over trousers, putting a jumper on the wrong way around etc. This can be extended to snack time, when the adult could try to cut fruit with a fork. The children should be encouraged to identify and express the absurdity and come up with a solution. This can be a fun activity with lots of humour and enjoyment.

- Create other problem scenarios in the Early Years setting, such as asking the children to paint without providing the paint, look at a book without providing any book etc.

- Look at funny picture scenarios and encourage the children to identify what is wrong. For example, the car may have square wheels instead of round wheels, the television may be upside down etc. You may need to model answers and supply the necessary vocabulary.

- As a whole group, plan for an outing or activity such as a party. Encourage the children to identify what is needed and to organise the event. You should provide support and guidance where necessary.

Predicting and inferring

Predicting and inferring refer to the ability to anticipate and express what may happen in events and scenarios. For example, in a picture of a man climbing a ladder with one step broken, the child should predict that the man might fall off the ladder. This is a more complex component of language development and requires a child to have sufficient language and thinking skills.

For children with speech and language delay, this less concrete use of language often poses difficulties.

Activities to develop predicting and inferring:

- In familiar, real-life events, encourage the children to predict what might happen, for example, if the child spills milk during snack time, you could discuss solutions, such as wiping the milk up with a cloth, vacuuming it up or leaving it on the floor. The child needs to choose the most suitable option. Children with a greater range of language skills can come up with their own solutions.

- During story time, when reading unfamiliar books to the children, stop after a few pages and encourage them to think what will happen next. To continue the theme, they could be asked to draw pictures of possible endings to the story.

Speech sounds

Typically, children's speech sound system may not be fully developed until seven years of age. All children simplify words for ease of articulation. These simplification processes can be described in well-defined stages.

For many children, for a variety of reasons, their speech sounds may be delayed and even disordered, that is, not following a typical pattern of development. Between the ages of three and three and a half, most speech sound work will focus on developing listening and auditory discrimination skills rather than production.

As the child's vocabulary develops, so too should their speech sound system, as they are able to practise the sounds in more words. If you are concerned about a child's speech sounds, it is advised that you seek advice from your local speech and language therapist who can assess and offer further guidance.

A few useful general tips:

- When the child mispronounces a word, acknowledge their attempt and repeat back the correct model, emphasising the target sound. Most importantly, do not get the child to repeat the adult model.

- If the child is substituting one sound for another, for example /p/ for /f/, i.e. saying 'pish' for 'fish' and 'pour' for 'four', then stress all the 'f' sounds in your own speech when talking to the child. Again, do not encourage the child to repeat your model.

- Try to avoid telling children that you have not understood them, but rather encourage them to show or tell you in a different way. This should help avoid frustration at not being understood. Practitioners should look out for signs of withdrawal and/or avoiding words or situations, as some children may be aware of their difficulties and avoid interactions.

Tried and tested tips

Here are some useful strategies to promote effective communication with a child with speech and language delay:

- Call the child's name and encourage him/her to look at you before you engage further.

- Keep distractions to a minimum: turn down music, limit the number of activities on display, put away resources that are not being used, keep wall and table displays relevant and so on.

- Use natural gestures and meaningful sounds to promote effective communication.

- Remember to give simple, clear instructions and repeat critical information, for example, when you want the child to get their coat and shoes, you may say, 'Jimmy, get your coat and your shoes … coat and shoes', repeating the important information.

- Highlight targeted sounds and words by emphasising them, for example, if your target sound is 's', you may say, 'Jimmy, where's your **sock**?' or if your target word is 'on', you may say 'Jimmy, put the cup **on** the table'.

- Use visual timetables. These can be particularly effective in an Early Years provision. Photos, signs and symbols are used to indicate to the child what activity comes next and to let them know when activities will finish. Ask a speech and language therapist for further advice and information regarding the use of photos, signs and symbols.

- Use songs and rhymes. These can be used to teach and reinforce new concepts and vocabulary in a fun way. Familiar rhymes can be used to encourage early language skills, such as eye contact, joint attention and simple vocabulary. For the older child, themes can be introduced through the use of music and songs, for example, the alphabet song.

- Use an interesting and animated voice. This can be a useful tool in gaining and maintaining attention, and highlighting new concepts, sounds and vocabulary.

How to ensure successful learning in the EYFS

Having a child with a speech and language delay in your provision does not necessarily mean that you have to spend prolonged, individual time with that child on a daily basis – regular, small blocks of time, either individually or in a group, working on specific targets, can be equally valuable. Children who have a Statement of Special Educational Needs may have additional allocated hours for support.

With a bit of planning and a whole lot of creativity, you can differentiate almost any activity, goal or theme to the level that each of the children in your provision is at.

The activities, ideas and tips in this book also offer you the opportunity to engage all the children, or a small group of children, in a language-rich experience, while targeting specific goals at the level of the child with speech and language delay.

Here are some useful tips and strategies to use during a range of provision-based activities, both inside and outside the provision.

Tips

- During circle time, don't choose a child with speech and language delay (including delayed attention and listening) first or last, as:

  - they will have to wait a long time until the activity is finished or they will have to wait a long time until it is their turn.

  - they will not have a language model for the activity.

  Choose the child with a speech and language delay later on in the activity, such as fourth of fifth, so they do not have to wait too long for their turn and have peer and adult models to copy.

  As the child's speech and language skills develop, offer them the opportunity to have a go first, as most children like to start.

- **Sit the child with a speech and language delay between you and a child with good attention and listening skills**. This will allow you to monitor the child's understanding and participation, as well as reducing distractions for the child.

- **Plan how to differentiate activities.** This can be done by:

  - **adapting materials** for the child with speech and language delay, such as using books with picture support, blocks to encourage counting and one-to-one number recognition. Also, the use of large toys as opposed to small toys may be more appropriate for children with speech and language delay. It is important to grade materials for their complexity, for example, using objects followed by photos, then pictures followed by symbols, to teach new vocabulary and concepts.

- **adapting your expectations** and specifically targeting your outcomes for each child. For example, in circle time, when talking about the life cycle of a butterfly, you may expect some children to recall the cycle independently in a coherent sequence. For others, the expectation may be for them to label the stages using single words, picture prompts, or using pointing and/or cues from the Early Years practitioner.

- **adapting the level** for every activity. Think and plan how to make an activity easier and, where necessary, more challenging.

- Think and plan how you can **teach the same concepts in different multi-sensory ways**. Incorporating all the senses will help learning at all levels. It is important to review and reinforce ideas and concepts regularly. Additionally, when giving instructions, check that the child has understood what is required by asking simple questions.

- Where possible, **pre-teach and send home topic vocabulary**. For example, if the whole group is exploring minibeasts, before the topic is introduced, send home vocabulary related to this subject and provide the child with specific activities to familiarise them with the new vocabulary and concepts.

- Observe and **find out what motivates and interests the child** with speech and language delay. Take note of what they are successful in and try to plan activities with these in mind as the child will be more likely to achieve. It is also important to **identify their learning styles and schemas** through careful observation. Your planning should take this into consideration as it will enable you to engage the child's attention and facilitate their learning. Children learn in different ways. In the Early Years setting, it is good to supply the group with activities that take into account different types of learning style, such as:

  - using visual timetables, sign, gesture, pictures, symbols and so on

  - doing any practical work or experiments before you do any written or oral/aural work, such as go on a nature walk before you draw or write about insects and bugs, do a cooking activity before you write the recipe and so on

  - using sensory cues, particularly for tactile learners. This might include the use of sand, water, shaving foam and other materials.

- Always **cue a child with speech and language delay** in first. Suggestions include:

  - saying the child's name before you give them an instruction or ask for a response

  - giving the child a gentle physical prompt to gain their attention, perhaps gently touching the child's arm

  - waiting until you have gained their attention before giving an instruction

  - using key words, such as 'look', 'listen' and 'think' to encourage good listening

  - using picture symbols that will help children with speech and language delay to remember and use the rules of good listening – the symbols can also be used to cue the child to 'look', 'listen' and 'think'

o allowing the child with speech and language delay time to process thoughts, ideas and instructions.

● Where possible, try to **reduce distractions** such as:

o excessive background noise. Try to consider the noise level when expecting a child with speech and language delay to listen and attend. Early Years settings are often busy with high levels of background noise. However, reducing the noise level is important when trying to promote listening skills. Allocate an area in the Early Years setting where the children know that they have to use quiet voices and not be physically active. In this way, you are creating a space where noise levels are lowered, allowing children to listen and attend.

o equipment and unused toys. Children with speech and language delay may become distracted by pictures, toys and equipment that has been left out. Where possible, remove or cover up anything unrelated to the activity. In circle time or classroom activities, once an object has been used, remove it from the child's sight so as not to distract them. For younger children, encourage them to wave 'goodbye' to toys and objects once they have finished with them. Once again, in this way you are removing visual distractions.

● **Adapt your language level** to that of the child when giving instructions and expecting responses. For example, if a three-year-old child is talking at the two-word level, that is, they are using word combinations such as 'teddy sitting', your instructions to the child should be short and simple.

● When doing group work, try to **ensure that the child with a speech and language delay is in a group** with other children who are effective communicators.

● Whenever possible, try to **feedback on progress and relevant activities to the child's parents/carers** and other professionals involved with the child to encourage generalisation of skills.

● **Identify and involve the friends** of the child with speech and language delay. These children can often be used to encourage and support the child with speech and language delay and to promote their social confidence.

● When you start an activity, **make the task achievable** for a child with speech and language delay so they can feel successful. You can then increase the complexity gradually. Children with speech and language delay may have had frequent experiences of not achieving and of communication breakdown. This often impacts upon their self-confidence and can cause high expectations of failure.

Remember to encourage the child and praise all their attempts in a way that is motivating and meaningful to them.

Important words explained simply

Bilingual children: refers to children who regularly use two languages in everyday communication.

Cognition: refers to children's learning and thinking skills.

Echolalia: is a term used to refer to children who repeat spoken or signed words, sentences and phrases without functional meaning.

Expressive language: refers to children's use and expression of language. This can take on different forms, such as making meaningful sounds, producing words and sentences, and having conversations, either by speaking or signing. This does not take speech clarity into consideration.

Eye pointing: refers to a way of communicating using eye gaze to select, indicate choices, show information and request.

Functional language: refers to the use of language with a meaning attached i.e. using language to comment, request, question and share interests.

Language: refers to children's understanding of receptive and expressive language (see corresponding terms). It does not include children's speech sounds/articulation.

Language delay: is a term used to describe children's communication progress when it follows a typical pattern of development, but at a slower rate than would be expected.

Language disorder/Specific Language Impairment (SLI): speech and language disorder or Specific Language Impairment are terms used to describe children whose speech and language development is distorted and progress is unequivocally slow.

Makaton: refers to a way of communicating and supporting understanding using sign.

Pre-verbal skills: refers to the early communication skills required for successful interactions – eye contact, play, turn-taking, attention and listening skills.

Receptive language: refers to children's ability to understand what they see and hear – their understanding of facial expressions, body language, situations, words and sentences – whether spoken or signed.

Situational understanding: refers to children's understanding of familiar routines, events and actions.

Specific praise: is a term used to refer to commenting very precisely on what children have done well.

Speech: refers to the way sounds are produced, both on their own and in words or sentences, and how the production affects a speaker's clarity.

Stages of speech and language development

These charts are intended to provide parents and practitioners with a guide on what to expect at different ages and stages of speech and language for children between birth and five years. The first stage (Birth to 11 months) is included to support parents and practitioners in identifying early potential concerns that may reveal themselves and which may require particular intervention. Information was gathered and lists adapted from *Shipley and McAfee (2004)* and *Early Years Foundation Stage: Setting the Standards for Learning, Development and Care for children from birth to 5 years (DCSF 2008)* and *the Early Years Foundation Stage Profile Handbook (DCFS 2008)*.

Birth to 11 months

Attention and listening	Understanding	Talking	Speech sounds	Play and social interaction
Turns towards a familiar sound	Recognises parents' and other close adults'/children's voices	Makes sounds such as gurgling, babbling	Experiments and explores making sounds	Makes sounds e.g. gurgling, crying and cooing to express interests, wants, likes and dislikes
Startled by loud noises	Shows excitement at sound of approaching voices	Makes noises to get attention	Uses a range of two-syllable babble e.g. 'dada', 'muma' and begins to use single words	Senses others' emotions and often responds accordingly, e.g. may smile, laugh, quieten, frown or cry
Looks at faces when someone talks	Understands simple familiar routines e.g. meal times, bath times, going out	Responds with vocalisations when talked to	Uses babble to communicate with adults and siblings 'ba-ba, na-na, ga-ga'	Enjoys and responds to action rhymes, lullabies and songs
Begins to locate source of different sounds	Understands commonly used words such as 'all gone', 'hello', 'no' and 'bye bye'	Tries to communicate by gestures e.g. waving and pointing	Starts using speech intentionally for the first time after 7 months	Begins to copy lip patterns of the speaker
Takes pleasure in listening to a variety of sounds	Shows recognition of words for common items (e.g. cup, shoe and baby) after 7 months	Starts copying some adult intonation (i.e. pitch and rhythm) speech patterns after 7 months		Adopts 'turns' in babble conversations
Follows and reacts to movement and sounds	Recognises sound of own name, may stop or look at speaker	Will imitate sounds and take turns in sound-making play		Carries out the same action over and over again to explore the properties of an object e.g. banging, shaking, mouthing
Easily distracted e.g. by loud noises, objects/people	Starts understanding 'no' and 'hot' after 7 months.	Towards the end of the first year starts using some single words (mostly object words) and learned phrases (e.g. 'all gone', 'bye bye')		

Attention and listening	Understanding	Talking	Speech sounds	Play and social interaction
Responds and enjoys music and songs	Understands an increasing range of simple words and common phrases in context, e.g. 'drink', 'juice', 'tidy up', 'come here'	Reaches or points with speech sounds to indicate needs, desires and to share interests	From 8 months uses a large variety of babbling sounds	From 8 months starts using gestures and vocalisations to express wants/needs
Enjoys noisy toys		Between 8 and 12 months starts using some single words and learned phrases e.g. 'all gone'	From 8 months starts using a range of two syllable babble e.g. 'dada', 'mama'	Enjoys being with familiar adults, although increasingly plays alone
Listens and responds to simple information/ instructions, e.g. 'Ben, put on your shoes', Mohammed, give to daddy'	Between 8 and 12 months starts showing recognition of some words for every day objects	From 8 months starts copy-ing some adult intonation (i.e. pitch and rhythm) speech patterns	Between 8 and 12 months starts using single words	Increasingly makes requests for more of a motivating item
	Between 8 and 12 months starts showing understanding of 'no' and 'hot'		Many sounds are simplified in a predictive, understandable manner, e.g. 'nanna' for banana	Can sustain turn-taking games for longer
Understands key words in short phrases		Still babbles		Likes and responds to verbal and non-verbal praise, e.g. hugs, clapping, "well done!" smiles and kissing
Relies on gesture and prompts to support understanding of first words	Understands more words than they can say	Uses 10-20 single words correctly, although they may not be clear	May be able to use sounds on their own but not in words. E.g. can say 'sssss' but may still say 'dock' for 'sock'	
	Understands common requests, e.g. 'Johnnie sit down', 'Raheen coat on' 'Alice, give me teddy'	Able to copy words and gestures from adults	Omits some initial sounds and most final sounds in imitation or words	Shows excitement and interest in familiar, motivating games
	Can point to a range of objects and pictures when asked	After 13 months starts us-ing long strings of babble which mirror the intonation, pitch and loudness of adult speech (i.e. jargon) inter-spersed with real words e.g. 'the cat, babble out, babble'		Enjoys cause-and-effect and anticipation games and activities e.g. round and round the garden, waiting for a tickle
	After 13 months can identify 1 - 3 body parts on self	After 13 months starts using echolalia	Produces mostly unintelligible speech	Begins to use play objects appropriately e.g. feeding themselves and others, pushing cars along
			Babbling will still be used	Enjoys and responds to familiar stories and songs

Attention and listening	Understanding	Talking	Speech sounds	Play and social interaction
Able to attend to an activity of their choice for longer periods of time but may not tolerate adult direction	Understanding of new words develops rapidly	Towards 24 months uses 50 – 100 or more words	Uses speech sounds such as /p/, /b/, /d/, /m/, /n/, /h/ and /w/ at the beginning of words words, e.g. 'ball, baby, more, milk, 'bum, poo'	Pretend play develops using toys as props e.g. feeding dolly, feeding teddy, stirring food, driving and crashing cars
Can select two toys/items on request when pre-sented with a range of items, e.g. 'Give me pig and horse'	By around 2 years the child can have a receptive vocabulary of 200-500 words	Begins to join 2-3 words together to make short phrases e.g. 'sit-down baby' 'more juice' 'no sleeping'	Most vowels are present in words	Is able to do simple pull-out puzzles
Can identify familiar nursery and action rhymes from their tunes or opening phrases	Can identify a range of about 5 body parts, e.g. fingers, toes and nose of themselves and later on other's e.g. dolly's hair	From around19 months starts to combine action words and nouns e.g. 'baby eating'	Sounds continue to be simplified e.g. 'fish 'becomes 'pish' and 'sock' becomes 'dock'	Able to build block towers
	Can follow a two-part instruction such as 'Get the train and give it to Eric.'	Babble lessens as their use of real words increases but may still use jargon/ non-sense words	Uses pitch and intonation appropriately to express basic emotions such as anger and contentment	Enjoys looking at books
	Starts to understand action words in a phrase, such as 'Baby drinking'	Starts to use own name		Self confidence develops and enjoys being with others
	Understands simple commentary in the context of an activity e.g. 'Mary's kicking ball'	From 19 months names some familiar objects		May get frustrated when they can't get their own way – this may result in tantrums
	From 19 months starts answering 'What's that?' questions	Starts to use the possessive pronoun 'mine'		Aware of and responds to emotions and facial expressions
		From 19 months starts using appropriate intonation (i.e. pitch and rhythm) for questions		

Attention and listening	Understanding	Talking	Speech sounds	Play and social interaction
Will focus on one activity at a time and can shift attention to another activity with support	Understands 500-900 or more words	Uses between 50 and 250 words including descriptive language and time, space and function words	Speech becoming clearer, although may still struggles to say speech sounds such as /l/, /r/, /w/, /y/, /f/, /th/, /s/, /sh/, /ch/ and /j/	Is able to hold a simple conversation but tends to jump from topic to topic
Can listen for longer periods and recall information	Starts to understands simple concepts including in/on/under, big/l ttle, wet/ dry and common colours	Talks about the here and now. May verbalise toilet needs	Leaves out some unstressed parts of speech, such as 'banana' becoming 'nana' and 'tomato' becoming 'mato'	Is more interested in playing with other children on their own terms
They can recall three items from a spoken request	Starts understanding the concepts 'one' and 'all'	Uses simple statements and requests		Shows emotions using both words and actions towards adults and peers
Enjoys listening to simple stories on a CD	Can identify several body parts on self and named others	Asks one to two word questions	Consistently includes initial sounds in words (even when unclear)	Beginning to link actions together in their play e.g. kiss baby and put baby to bed, feed baby and wipe her mouth
	Understands up to three key word instructions	Links 2-4 words together in phrases	Begins to use end-sounds of words more consistently	
	Can respond to a request of up to three items	Uses intonation, rhythm and phrasing to make themselves understood e.g. 'where's the ball gone?' with rising intonation (increased range of pitch)	Still inconsistent in the use of sounds in the middle of words	Enjoys imitative play and 'helping' adults with every day tasks
	Understands simple 'who' and 'what' and 'where' questions		Uses vowels correctly	
	Understands a simple story when supported with pictures	Beginning to use more pronouns	Often speaks with a loud voice	
	Anticipates key events and phrases in familiar rhymes and stories	Begins to use prepositions, past tense verbs, plurals	Repetitions often present in spoken language-especially starters such as 'I' and first syllables of words such as 'da-da-daddy' (i.e. may stutter or stammer when thinking what to say)	
	Can match some simple shapes and colours	Sings along to familiar rhymes		

30 to 50 months

Attention and listening	Understanding	Talking	Speech sounds	Play and social interaction
Beginning to listen to others in one-to-one situations and small groups	Understands up to 1200 to 2000 or more words	Uses up to 800 to 1500 or more words	Speech continues to develop, may still have difficulties with, /l/, /th/, /ch/, and /sh/	Is able to turn-take and share more easily with adults and peers
Can shift attention between activities spontaneously without adult prompts	Understands questions or instructions with two to three parts, e.g. "tidy up, wash your hands and line up"	Uses sentences of four to six words e.g. 'I want to have the red one'	May use some sound blends such as /mb/ in 'bumb', /sm/ in 'small' and /dr/ in 'dragon'	Starts conversations with adults and peers
Can recall 4-5 items on request	Understands "why" questions	Asks and answers questions (mostly what, where and why questions)	Some substitutions are still made, e.g. /gween/ for 'green'	Enjoys playing and interacting with peers
	Understands sentences in the past, present and future, e.g. 'yesterday we went swimming, tomorrow we're going to the park?' (towards four years)	From 36 months starts using 'is', 'are' and 'am' appropriately in sentences	Whispers	Able to disagree with adults by using words and actions
	From 36 months starts understanding object function such as could identify a brush from lots of objects when asked for something to clean floor	Uses regular past tense 'ed' to express to past events	Distinguishes letters of personal significance (i.e. initial letter of their names and other words that start with this letter), e.g. 'look it's the same as my name, it's a 'k''	Plays imaginatively acting out scenes and events with props and puppets
	Is conscious of the past and future	Can recall and recount own experiences and share with others		Is able to substitute one object for another in play, e.g. using a block of wood for a phone
		Can tell two events in order		Uses language to express emotion
		Still uses some irregular plurals		
		Uses some future tense verbs		
		Uses some conjunctions such as 'and'		
		Can express simple emotions. E.g. 'Kay's sad'		
		Asks many questions and often demands detailed responses		

40 to 60 months

Attention and listening	Understanding	Talking	Speech sounds	Play and social interaction
Can do an activity whilst listening to spoken instructions or commentary	Are less dependent on pictures to understand stories	Asks for clarification if they do not understand a word or instruction	Speech is clear to all listeners with a few speech sound errors, for example /th/, /r/ and three consonant combinations e.g. 'scratch, strong, strawberry'	Chooses own friends
Can listen to what others say and respond to what they have heard	Is able to understand sequencing instruction words 'who's first? What happens next?'	Can use language to describe, request, ask questions and express disagreement		Enjoys playing with friends and generally co-operates
Answers simple questions about a story they have listened to	Can answer questions about function	Talks more about experiences, e.g. what happened at school, home etc.	Produces consonants with 90% accuracy	Imaginative play becomes more sophisticated and involves more peers
	Able to predict	Increasingly accurately relays OR re-tells a story	The occurrence of sound omissions and substitutions reduces significantly over time	Takes turns in longer conversations
	Can understand more complex humour, laughs at jokes that are told	Uses well formed sentences with some grammatical errors, e.g. "I saw 3 sheeps"	Still frequently omits middle consonants in words	Uses language for a variety of functions – to gain information, negotiate, discuss feeling/ideas and give opinions
	From 48 months understands 2800 or more words	From 48 months uses 900 to 2000 or more words with four to eight word sentences	Speech is usually intelligible to strangers	Understands social conventions e.g. 'using', 'may I ......', 'please' and 'thank you'
	Recognises many colours and shapes	Uses some irregular plurals, possessive pronouns and future tense	After 60 months:	Beginning to be able to negotiate
	Understands concept of numbers up to 10	From 48 months mostly uses grammatically correct sentences	Occasionally still reverses sounds	Can initiate, maintain and change a topic of conversation
	Counts to 10 by rote		Sings entire songs and recites nursery rhymes	
			Easily communicates with adults and peers	

Resources

Agencies

These agencies provide information to support children's communication and educational needs.

www.speech-lang.org.uk
The Speech, Language and Hearing Centre at Christopher Place is a centre for babies and children under five who have a hearing impairment and/or a speech, language and communication delay.
The Centre follows a child-centred programme that combines teaching and therapy from an interdisciplinary professional team and where a close partnership with the whole family is central to their work.

www.ican.org.uk
ICAN provides information about specialist Early Years and school settings, training, resources (some of which are free) and offers assessments.

www.rcslt.org.uk
The Royal College of Speech and Language Therapy provides information on speech and language therapy, and useful links to support and voluntary organisations.

www.helpwithtalking.com
Help with Talking provides general information about speech and language therapy, a list of private speech and language therapists, details of voluntary organisations, and courses and articles.

www.sen-for-schools.co.uk
sen-for-schools is a website aimed at supporting Special Needs professionals in schools.

www.teachernet.gov.uk
The SEN Code of Practice publication provides practical Special Educational Needs support for SENCOs and all school staff.

www.surestart.gov.uk
Sure Start is the government programme to deliver the best start in life for every child by bringing together early education, childcare, health and family support.

http://textsandexams.qca.org.uk
The **QCA's tests** and exam report website provides you with more information about the EYFS profile.

www.earlysupport.org.uk
Early Support is a website that provides information, support, materials, training and advice for families with young disabled children.

www.everychildmatters.gov.uk
Every Child Matters is a government programme for a national framework to support the joining-up of children's services, such as education, health and social care.

www.publications.teachernet.gov.uk
This is an **online publications for schools** service that links directly into the Department for Children, Schools and Families' ordering hotline and distribution centre, which allows users to view or download the publications that are relevant to them. Registered users can also order copies and receive email alerts to the latest documents.

www.dcsf.gov.uk/slcnaction
This site looks at **Better Communication: An Action Plan to Improve Services for Children and Young
People with Speech, Language and Communication Needs,** which was published by the government in December 2008 following the Review of Services for Children and Young People with Speech, Language and Communication Needs (SLCN) by John Bercow MP.

www.ofsted.gov.uk
The **Office for Standards in Education, Children's Services and Skills** inspects and regulates care for children and young people, and inspects education and training for learners of all ages. Ofsted aims to raise aspirations and contribute to the long-term achievement of ambitious standards and better life chances for service users.

www.makaton.org
This website provides information on the use of **Makaton** signing and baby signing.

www.nasen.org.uk
The National Association for Special Educational Needs aims to promote the education, training, advancement and development of all those with special and additional support needs.

Books and Websites

Here is a selection of books and websites that will provide support, advice and a range of ideas and resources to promote communication and play. High-street toy shops also have a variety of useful toys.

www.nurseryworld.co.uk
Nursery World publishes a range of books, booklets and resource packs written especially for Early Years professionals.

 'How to Identify and Support Children with Speech and Language Difficulties' by Jane Speaks.
This book is aimed at those working with babies, toddlers and young children in the Early Years setting. It provides advice and information on supporting children with language difficulties.

'Speech and Language Difficulties in the Classroom' by Deirdre Martin Carol Miller.
This book is aimed at those working with children with speech and language difficulties. It provides information and strategies to use in the classroom setting.

'You Make the Difference in Helping Your Child Learn' by Ayala Manolson with Barb Ward and Nancy Dodington. This book is aimed at parents and carers of babies, toddlers and young children. It gives basic information and practical ideas on how best to promote effective communication.

'It Takes Two to Talk: A Parent's Guide to Helping Children Communicate' by Ayala Manolson.
A book aimed at parents, providing information and activities to promote language development in young children.

www.winslow-cat.com
This website provides educational, social and health professionals with resources.

www.wescona.com
Wescona has a variety of toys and products to develop communication, play and sensory motor skills.

www.ldalearning.com
This website shows a range of resources to help develop language, literacy, mathematical skills, motor skills and PSHE.

www.eduzone.co.uk
Eduzone provides a range of resources to develop language, literacy, mathematical skills, motor skills and PSHE.

www.taskmasteronline.co.uk
This website contains a range of resources to help develop language, literacy, mathematical skills and motor skills.

www.sensetoys.com
Sense Toys has a selection of multi-sensory verbal and non-verbal toys to help develop communication.

www.rompa.com
This is a multi-sensory resource for a range of developmental, sensory, movement and soft play toys.

http://talk-pod.com
This website provides information and activities for Talking Tins. Talking Tins allow you to record and play back your own voice messages, music or sound effects, and are effective resources that are proving to help children of all ages to develop their speaking and listening skills.

www.childrensdisabilities.info
This website aims to support parents of children with communication difficulties. It provides a directory of articles, books, advice, information and groups for those caring for children with communication difficulties.

References

Basic Skills Agency (2002) *Summary Report of Survey into Young Children's Skills on Entry to Education.*

Bercow Report: *A Review of Services for Children and Young People (0–19) with Speech, Language and Communication Needs.*

Cooper, J., Moodley, M. And Reynell, J. (1978) *Helping Language Development. Edward Arnold Ltd.*

DFES (2005) *Foundation Stage Profile 2005 National Results (Provisional) National Statistics Office.*

Early Years Foundation Stage (2008) Setting the Standards for Learning, Development and Care for Children from Birth to Five. Department of Education and Skills.

Early Years Foundation Stage Profile Handbook (DCFS, 2008) Goldschmied, E. (1989) Treasure basket

Manning-Morton, J. and Thorp, M. (2001) Key Times – *A Framework for Developing High Quality Provision for Children Under Three Years Old.* Camden Under Threes Development Group and The University of North London.

Law, J., Boyle, J., Harris, F., Harkness, A. and Nye C. (2000) *Prevalence and Natural History of Primary Speech and Language Delay: Findings from a Systemic Review of the Literature,* IJLCD, vol. 36.Years, IJCLD, vol. 27, no. 1.

Lindsay, G. and Dockrell, J. with Mackie, C. and Letchford, B. (2002) *Educational Provision for Children with Specific Speech and Language Difficulties in England and Wales Cedar and Institute of Education,* University of London.

Locke, A., Ginsborg, J. and Peers, I. (2002) *Development and Disadvantage: Implications for Early Years,* IJCLD, vol. 27, no. 1. Manning-Morton, J. and Thorp, M. (2001) *Information on schemas,* University of North London.

Johnson, R. (2009) 'The Rapper's Way', Christopher Place, Speech Language and Hearing Centre.

The Communication Trust Conference: March 2008, *Developing a Workforce to Support Speech, Language and Communication for all Children.*

Other titles in this series

Including Children with:

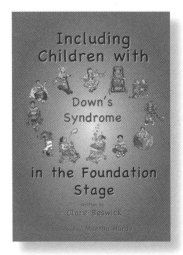

**Down's Syndrome
by Clare Beswick**

9781904187905

**Asperger's Syndrome
by Clare Beswick**

9781905019113

**Autistic Spectrum
Disorders (ASD)
by Clare Beswick**

9781904187288

**Attention and
Behaviour
Difficulties (ABD)
by Maureen Garner**

9781905019014

**Working Within
the P Levels
by Kay Holman and
Janet Beckett**

9781905019380

**Developmental
Co-ordination
Disorder (Dyspraxia)
by Sharon Drew**

9781905019458

All available from www.acblack.com/featherstone